CORE CONNECTIONS GEOMETR
Parent Guide with Extra Practice

D1284341

Managing Editors / Authors

Leslie Dietiker (First Edition)
Boston University
Boston, MA

Michael Kassarjian (Second Edition)
CPM Educational Program
Encino, CA

Contributing Authors

Elizabeth Coyner
Christian Brothers High School
Sacramento, CA

Lew Douglas
The College Preparatory School
Oakland, CA

David Gulick
Phillips Exeter Academy
Exeter, NH

Lara Lomac
Phillip and Sala Burton Academic High
School, San Francisco, CA

Damian Molinari
Phillip and Sala Burton Academic High
School, San Francisco, CA

Jason Murphy-Thomas
George Washington High School
San Francisco, CA

Leslie Nielson
Issaquah High School
Issaquah, WA

Karen O' Connell
San Lorenzo High School
San Lorenzo, CA

Ward Quincy
Gideon Hauser Jewish Day School
Palo Alto, CA

Barbara Shreve
San Lorenzo High School
San Lorenzo, CA

Michael Titelbaum
University of California
Berkeley, CA

Editor

Bob Petersen
CPM Educational Program
Sacramento, CA

Technical Assistants

Hannah Coyner

Sarah Maile

Aubrie Maze

Cover Art

Kevin Coffey
San Francisco, CA

Program Directors

Leslie Dietiker
Boston University
Boston, MA

Lori Hamada
CPM Educational Program
Fresno, CA

Brian Hoey
CPM Educational Program
Sacramento, CA

Judy Kysh, Ph.D.
Departments of Education and Mathematics
San Francisco State University, CA

Tom Sallee, Ph.D.
Department of Mathematics
University of California, Davis

Based on *Geometry Connections Parent Guide* © 2006
and *Geometry Connections Extra Practice* © 2008

Editors of Parent Guide

Brian Hoey   Karen Wootten

Editor of Extra Practice

Bob Petersen

Technical Manager

Rebecca Harlow

Technical Assistants

Erica Andrews   Elizabeth Burke   Carrie Cai
Daniel Cohen   Elizabeth Fong   Rebecca Harlow
Michael Leong   Thomas Leong   Marcos Rojas
Susan Ryan

1 2 3 4 5 6   18 17 16 15 14 13

Printed in the United States of America   ISBN: 978-1-60328-110-2

Introduction to the Parent Guide with Extra Practice

Welcome to the *Core Connections Geometry Parent Guide with Extra Practice*. The purpose of this guide is to assist you should your child need help with homework or the ideas in the course. We believe all students can be successful in mathematics as long as they are willing to work and ask for help when they need it. We encourage you to contact your child's teacher if your student has additional questions that this guide or other resources do not answer.

This guide was written to address the major topics in each chapter of the textbook. Each section begins with a title bar and the lesson(s) in the book that it addresses. In many cases the explanation box at the beginning of the section refers you to one or more Math Notes boxes in the student text for additional information about the fundamentals of the idea. Detailed examples follow a summary of the concept or skill and include complete solutions. The examples are similar to the work your child has done in class. Additional problems, with answers, are provided for your child to practice.

There will be some topics that your child understands quickly and some concepts that may take longer to master. The big ideas of the course take time to learn. This means that students are not necessarily expected to master a concept when it is first introduced. When a topic is first introduced in the textbook, there will be several problems to do for practice. Subsequent lessons and homework assignments will continue to practice the concept or skill over weeks and months so that *mastery will develop over time*.

Practice and discussion are required to understand mathematics. When your child comes to you with a question about a homework problem, often you may simply need to ask your child to read the problem and then ask her/him what the problem is asking. Reading the problem aloud is often more effective than reading it silently. When you are working problems together, have your child talk about the problems. Then have your child practice on his/her own.

Below is a list of additional questions to use when working with your child. These questions do not refer to any particular concept or topic. Some questions may or may not be appropriate for some problems.

- What have you been doing in class or during this chapter that might be related to this problem? Let's look at your notebook, class notes, Learning Log, and Toolkits. Do you have them?
- Were the other members of your team having difficulty with this as well? Can you call your study partner or someone from your study team?
- Have you checked the online homework help (in the student support section at www.cpm.org)?
- What have you tried? What steps did you take?
- What did not work? Why did it not work?
- Which words are most important? Why? What does this word/phrase tell you?
- What do you know about this part of the problem?
- Explain what you know right now.
- What is unknown? What do you need to know to solve the problem?
- How did the members of your study team explain this problem in class?
- What important examples or ideas were highlighted by your teacher?
- How did you organize your information? Do you have a record of your work?
- Can you draw a diagram or sketch to help you?
- Have you tried making a list, looking for a pattern, etc.?
- What is your estimate/prediction?
- Is there a simpler, similar problem we can do first?

If your student has made a start at the problem, try these questions:

- What do you think comes next? Why?
- What is still left to be done?
- Is that the only possible answer?
- Is that answer reasonable? Are the units correct?
- How could you check your work and your answer?

If you do not seem to be making any progress, you might try these questions.

- Let's look at your notebook, class notes, Learning Log, and Toolkit. Do you have them?
- Were you listening to your team members and teacher in class? What did they say?
- Did you use the class time working on the assignment? Show me what you did.
- Were the other members of your team having difficulty with this as well?
  Can you call your study partner or someone from your study team?

This is certainly not a complete list; you will probably come up with some of your own questions as you work through the problems with your child. Ask any question at all, even if it seems too simple to you.

To be successful in mathematics, students need to develop the ability to reason mathematically. To do so, students need to think about what they already know and then connect this knowledge to the new ideas they are learning. Many students are not used to the idea that what they learned yesterday or last week will be connected to today's lesson. Too often students do not have to do much thinking in school because they are usually just told what to do. When students understand that connecting prior learning to new ideas is a normal part of their education, they will be more successful in this mathematics course (and any other course, for that matter). The student's responsibilities for learning mathematics include the following:

- Actively contributing in whole class and study team work and discussion.
- Completing (or at least attempting) all assigned problems and turning in assignments in a timely manner.
- Checking and correcting problems on assignments (usually with their study partner or study team) based on answers and solutions provided in class and online.
- Asking for help when needed from his or her study partner, study team, and/or teacher.
- Attempting to provide help when asked by other students.
- Taking notes and using his/her Toolkit when recommended by the teacher or the text.
- Keeping a well-organized notebook.
- Not distracting other students from the opportunity to learn.

Assisting your child to understand and accept these responsibilities will help him or her to be successful in this course, develop mathematical reasoning, and form habits that will help her/him become a life-long learner.

Additional support for students and parents is provided at the CPM Homework Help website: http://www.cpm.org/students/homework/

The website provides a variety of complete solutions, hints, and answers. Some problems refer back to other similar problems. The homework help is designed to assist students to be able to do the problems but not necessarily do the problems for them.

ADDITIONAL SUPPORT

Consider these additional resources for assisting students with the CPM Educational Program:

- This *Core Connections Geometry Parent Guide with Extra Practice*. This booklet can be printed for no charge (or a bound copy ordered for $20) from the parent support section at www.cpm.org.

- CPM Homework Help website in the student support section at www.cpm.org. A variety of complete solutions, hints, and answers are provided. Some problems refer back to other similar problems. The homework help is designed to assist students to be able to do the problems but not necessarily do the problems for them.

- Checkpoints. The back of the student text has Checkpoint materials to assist students with skills they should master. The checkpoints are numbered to align with the chapter in the text. For example, the topics in Checkpoint 5A and Checkpoint 5B should be mastered while students complete Chapter 5.

- Resource Pages. The resource pages referred to in the student text can be found in the student support section of www.cpm.org.

- Previous tests. Many teachers allow students to examine their own tests from previous chapters in the course. Even if they are not allowed to bring these tests home, a student can learn much by analyzing errors on past tests.

- Math Notes in the student text. The Closure section at the end of each chapter in the student text has a list of the Math Notes in that chapter. Note that relevant Math Notes are sometimes found in other chapters than the one currently being studied.

- Glossary and index at the back of the student text.

- "Answers and Support" table. The "What Have I Learned" questions (in the closure section a the end of each chapter) are followed by an "Answers and Support" table that indicates where students can get more help with problems.

- After-school assistance. Some schools have after-school or at-lunch support programs for students. Ask the teacher.

- Other students. Consider asking your child to obtain the contact information for a couple other students in class.

- Parent Guides from previous courses. If your student needs help with the concepts from previous courses that are necessary preparation for this class, the *Parent Guides with Extra Practice* are available for no charge in the parent support section at www.cpm.org.

- ALEKS. For assistance with basic computational skills—particularly from previous courses—consider the ALEKS online class at www.aleks.com. ALEKS, developed by the University of California, uses artificial intelligence to know exactly which math computational skills your child has mastered, which are shaky, and which are new but within reach. ALEKS directs explanations, practice, and feedback as needed. ALEKS does not align with the topics in the CPM *Core Connections Geometry* text; ALEKS is useful for remediating basic skills from previous classes, but not particularly useful for assistance with the current geometry class. There is a charge for online access. ALEKS is not affiliated with the CPM Educational Program in any way.

Table of Contents

By asking questions such as "What happens if…?" and "What if I change …?" and answering them by trying different things, we can learn quite a lot about different shapes. In the first five lessons of Chapter 1, we explore symmetry, making predictions, perimeter, area, logical arguments, and angles by investigating each of these topics with interesting problems. These five lessons are introductory and help the teacher determine students' prior knowledge and preview some of the ideas that will be studied in this course. The following examples illustrate the geometry ideas in this section as well as some of the algebra review topics.

See the Math Notes boxes in Lessons 1.1.1, 1.1.2, 1.1.3, 1.1.4, and 1.1.5 for more information about the topics covered in this section.

Example 1

Suppose the rug in Figure 1 is enlarged as shown.

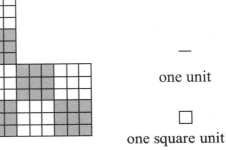

— one unit

□ one square unit

Figure 1   Figure 2   Figure 3

Fill in the table below to show how the perimeter and the area of the rug change as it is enlarged.

Figure Number	1	2	3	4	5	20
Perimeter (units)						
Area (square units)						

Perimeter is the distance (length) around the exterior of a figure on a flat surface while area is the number of non-overlapping square units needed to cover the figure. Perimeter is a unit of length, such as inches or centimeters, while area is measured in square units. Counting the units around the outside of Figure 1, we get a perimeter of 16 units. By counting the number of square units within Figure 1, we get an area of 12 square units. We do the same for the next two figures and record the information in the table.

Figure Number	1	2	3	4	5	20
Perimeter (units)	16	32	48			
Area (square units)	12	48	108			

Now comes the task of finding a pattern from these numbers. The perimeters seem to be connected to the number 16, while the areas seem connected to 12. Using this observation, we can rewrite the entries in the table and then extend the pattern to complete it as shown below.

Figure Number	1	2	3	4	5	20
Perimeter (in units)	1(16)	2(16)	3(16)	4(16)	5(16)	20(16)
Area (in square units)	1(12)	4(12)	9(12)	16(12)	25(12)	400(12)

Notice that the multipliers for the areas are the squares of the figure numbers.

Example 2

By using a hinged mirror and a piece of paper, students explored how a kaleidoscope works. The hinge should have been placed so that two edges of the mirror have the same length on the paper, forming an isosceles triangle. The reflection of the triangle in the mirror created shapes with varying numbers of sides. Through this investigation, students saw how angles are related to shapes. In particular, by opening the hinge of the mirror at a certain angle, students could create shapes in the mirror with specific numbers of sides. The hinge represented the angle at the center (or central angle) of the shape. (See Lesson 1.1.5 in the student text.) How many sides would the resulting shape have if the mirror was placed (1) At an obtuse angle (between 90° and 180°)? (2) At a right angle (exactly 90°)? (3) At an acute angle (less than 90°)?

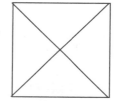

If the central angle is obtuse, the resulting figure is a triangle, so figures formed with this kind of angle are limited to three sides. If the hinge completely opens, it forms a straight angle (measuring 180°), and the figure is no longer a closed shape, but a line. As the hinge closes and forms a right angle, the figure adds another side, creating a quadrilateral As the hinge closes even further, the angle it makes is now acute. As the angle decreases in size this will create more sides on the polygon. It is possible to create a pentagon (five-sided figure), a hexagon (six-sided figure), and, in fact, any number of sides using acute angles of decreasing measures.

Example 3

Solve the equation for x: $2(x-4)+3(x+1)=43+x$

In solving equations such as the one above, we use the Distributive Property to simplify, combine like terms, and isolate the variables on one side of the equal sign and the constant terms (numbers) on the other side.

See the Math Notes box in Lesson 1.1.4 for another example.

$$2(x-4)+3(x+1)=43+x \quad \text{Distribute}$$
$$2x-8+3x+3=43+x$$
$$5x-5=43+x \quad \text{Simplify}$$
$$4x=48$$
$$\frac{4x}{4}=\frac{48}{4} \quad \text{Divide by 4}$$
$$x=12$$

Problems

Find the perimeter and area of each figure below.

1.

2.

3.

4.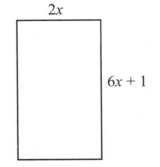

5. If the perimeter for the rectangle in problem 4 is 34 units, write an equation and solve for x.

6. Solve for x. Show the steps leading to your solution. $-2x + 6 = 5x - 8$

7. Solve for x. Show the steps leading to your solution. $3(2x - 1) + 9 = 4(x + 3)$

For problems 8-11, estimate the size of each angle to the nearest 10°.
A right angle is shown for reference so you should not need a protractor.
Then classify each angle as either acute, right, obtuse, straight, or circular.

8.

9.

10.

11.

Answers

1. Perimeter = 34 cm, Area = 42 square cm

2. Perimeter = 38 in., Area = 76 sq in.

3. Perimeter = 32 cm, Area = 38 square cm

4. Perimeter = $16x + 2$ units, Area = $2x(6x + 1)$ or $12x^2 + 2x$ units^2

5. $2(2x) + 2(6x + 1) = 34$, $x = 2$

6. $x = 2$

7. $x = 3$

8. $\approx 160°$, obtuse

9. $\approx 40°$, acute

10. $180°$, straight

11. $90°$, right

Studying transformations of geometric shapes builds a foundation for a key idea in geometry: congruence. In this introduction to transformations, the students explore three rigid motions: translations, reflections, and rotations. These explorations are done with tracing paper as well as with dynamic tools on the computer or other device. Students apply one or more of these motions to the original shape, creating its image in a new position without changing its size or shape. Rigid transformations also lead directly to studying symmetry in shapes. These ideas will help with describing and classifying geometric shapes later in the chapter.

See the Math Notes boxes in Lessons 1.2.2 and 1.2.4 for more information about rigid transformations.

Example 1

Decide which rigid transformation was used on each pair of shapes below. Some may be a combination of transformations.

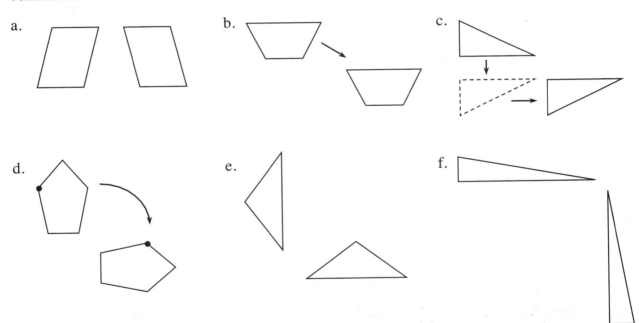

Identifying a single transformation is usually easy for students. In part (a), the parallelogram is reflected (flipped) across an invisible vertical line. (Imagine a mirror running vertically between the two figures. One figure would be the reflection of the other.) Reflecting a shape once changes its orientation. For example, in part (a), the two sides of the figure at left slant upwards to the right, whereas in its reflection at right, they slant upwards to the left. Likewise, the angles in the figure at left "switch positions" in the figure at right. In part (b), the shape is translated (or slid) to the right and down. The orientation remains the same, with all sides slanting the same.

Part (c) shows a combination of transformations. First the triangle is reflected (flipped) across an invisible horizontal line. Then it is translated (slid) to the right. The pentagon in part (d) has been rotated (turned) clockwise to create the second figure. Imagine tracing the first figure on tracing paper, then holding the tracing paper with a pin at one point below the first pentagon, then turning the paper to the right 90°. The second pentagon would be the result. Some students might see this as a reflection across a diagonal line. The pentagon itself could be, but with the added dot (small circle), the entire shape cannot be a reflection. If it had been reflected, the dot would have to be on the corner below the one shown in the rotated figure. The triangles in part (e) are rotations of each other (90° again). Part (f) shows another combination. The triangle is rotated (the shortest side becomes horizontal instead of vertical) and reflected.

Example 2

What will the figure at right look like if it is first reflected across line *l* and then the result is reflected across line *m*?

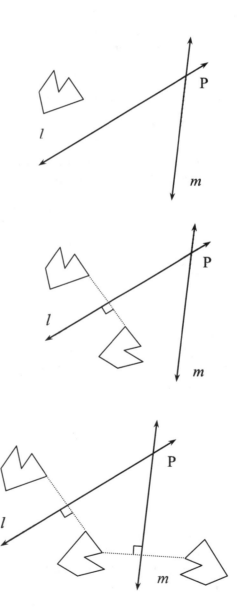

The first reflection is the new figure shown between the two lines. If we were to join each vertex (corner) of the original figure to its corresponding vertex on the second figure, those line segments would be perpendicular to line *l* and the vertices of (and all the other points in) the reflection would be the same distance away from *l* as they are in the original figure. One way to draw the reflection is to use tracing paper to trace the figure and the line *l*. Then turn the tracing paper over, so that line *l* is on top of itself. This will show the position of the reflection. Transfer the figure to your paper by tracing it. Repeat this process with line *m* to form the third figure by tracing.

As students discovered in class, reflecting twice like this across two intersecting lines produces a **rotation** of the figure about the point P. Put the tracing paper back over the original figure to line *l*. Put a pin or the point of a pen or pencil on the tracing paper at point P (the intersection of the lines of reflection) and rotate the tracing paper until the original figure will fit perfectly on top of the last figure.

Core Connections Geometry

Example 3

The shape at right is trapezoid ABCD. Translate the trapezoid 7 units to the right and 4 units up. Label the new trapezoid A′B′C′D′ and give the coordinates of its vertices. Is it possible to translate the original trapezoid in such a way to create A″B″C″D″ so that it is a reflection of ABCD? If so, what would be the reflecting line? Will this always be possible for any figure?

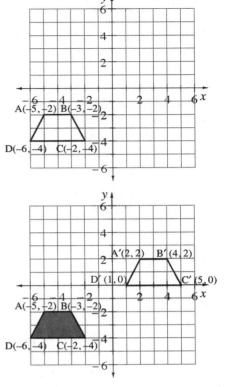

Translating (or sliding) the trapezoid 7 units to the right and 4 units up gives a new trapezoid A′(2, 2), B′(4, 2), C′(5, 0), and D′(1, 0). If we go back to trapezoid ABCD, we now wonder if we can translate it in such a way that we can make it look as if it were a reflection rather than a translation. Since the trapezoid is symmetrical, it is possible to do so. We can slide the trapezoid horizontally left or right. In either case, the resulting figure would look like a reflection.

This will not always work. It works here because we started with an isosceles trapezoid, which has a line of symmetry itself. Students explored which polygons have lines of symmetry, and which have rotational symmetry as well. Again, they used tracing paper as well as technology to investigate these properties.

Exploring these transformations and symmetrical properties of shapes helps to improve students' visualization skills. These skills are often neglected or taken for granted, but much of mathematics requires students to visualize pictures, problems, or situations. That is why we ask students to "visualize" or "imagine" what something might look like as well as practice creating transformations of figures.

Problems

Perform the indicated transformation on each polygon below to create a new figure. You may want to use tracing paper to see how the figure moves.

1. Rotate Figure A 90° clockwise about the origin.

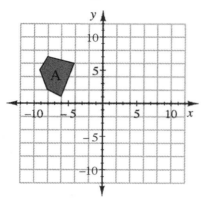

2. Reflect Figure B across line *l*.

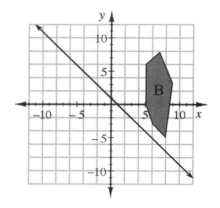

3. Translate Figure C 6 units left.

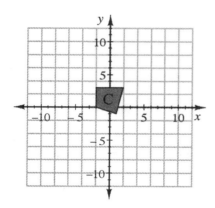

4. Rotate Figure D 270° clockwise about the origin $(0, 0)$.

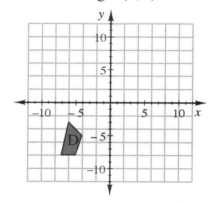

For problems 5 through 20, refer to the figures below.

Figure A

Figure B

Figure C

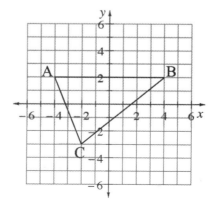

State the new coordinates after each transformation.

5. Translate Figure A left 2 units and down 3 units.

6. Translate Figure B right 3 units and down 5 units.

7. Translate Figure C left 1 unit and up 2 units.

8. Reflect Figure A across the x-axis.

9. Reflect Figure B across the x-axis.

10. Reflect Figure C across the x-axis.

11. Reflect Figure A across the y-axis.

12. Reflect Figure B across the y-axis.

13. Reflect Figure C across the y-axis.

14. Rotate Figure A 90° counterclockwise about the origin.

15. Rotate Figure B 90° counterclockwise about the origin.

16. Rotate Figure C 90° counterclockwise about the origin.

17. Rotate Figure A 180° counterclockwise about the origin.

18. Rotate Figure C 180° counterclockwise about the origin.

19. Rotate Figure B 270° counterclockwise about the origin.

20. Rotate Figure C 90° clockwise about the origin.

21. Plot the points A(3, 3), B(6, 1), and C(3, −4). Translate the triangle 8 units to the left and 1 unit up to create △A′B′C′. What are the coordinates of the new triangle?

22. How can you translate △ABC in the last problem to put point A″ at (4, −5)?

23. Reflect Figure Z across line l, and then reflect the new figure across line m. What are these two reflections equivalent to?

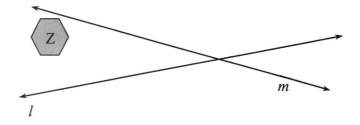

For each shape below, (*i*) draw all lines of symmetry, and (*ii*) describe its rotational symmetry if it exists.

24.

25.

26.

27.

Answers

1.

2.

3.

4.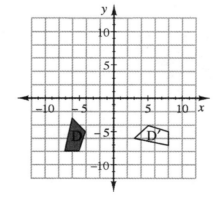

5. (−1, −3) (1, 2) (3, −1)

6. (−2, −3) (2, −3) (3, 0)

7. (−5, 4) (3, 4) (−3, −1)

8. (1, 0) (3, −4) (5, −2)

9. (−5, −2) (−1, −2) (0, −5)

10. (−4, −2) (4, −2) (−2, 3)

11. (−1, 0) (−3, 4) (−5, 2)

12. (5, 2) (1, 2) (0, 5)

13. (4, 2) (−4, 2) (2, −3)

14. (0, 1) (−4, 3) (−2, 5)

15. (−2, −5) (−5, 0) (−2, −1)

16. (−2, −4) (−2, 4) (3, −2)

17. (−1, 0) (−3, −4) (−5, −2)

18. (4, −2) (−4, −2) (2, 3)

19. (2, 5) (2, 1) (5, 0)

20. (2, 4) (2, −4) (−3, 2)

21. A′(5, −4), B′(−2, 2), C′(−5, −3)

22. Translate it 1 unit right and 8 units down.

23. The two reflections are the same as rotating Z about point X.

24. This has 180° rotational symmetry.

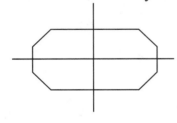

25. The one line of symmetry.
No rotational symmetry.

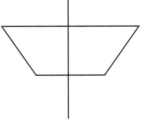

26. The circle has infinitely many lines of symmetry, every one of them illustrates reflection symmetry. It also has rotational symmetry for every possible degree measure.

27. This irregular shape has no lines of symmetry and does not have rotational symmetry, nor reflection symmetry.

Geometric shapes occur in many places. After studying them using transformations, students start to see certain characteristics of different shapes. In these lessons students look at shapes more closely, noticing similarities and differences. They begin to classify them using Venn diagrams. Students begin to see the need for precise names, which expands their geometric vocabulary. The last lesson introduces probability.

See the Math Notes box in Lesson 1.3.1 for more information about Venn diagrams.

Example 1

Decide which shapes from the Lesson 1.2.6 Resource Page belong in each section of the Venn diagram below.

#1: Two pairs of parallel sides   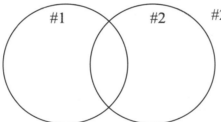   #2: All sides are the same length

Circle #1, represents all shapes on the resource page that have two pairs of parallel sides. There are four figures on the resource page that have this characteristic: the rectangle, the square, the rhombus, and the parallelogram. These shapes will be contained in circle #1. Circle #2 represents all shapes on the resource page that have sides all the same length. There are five figures with this 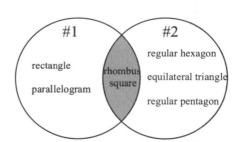 characteristic: the regular hexagon, the equilateral triangle, the square, the rhombus, and the regular pentagon. All five of these shapes will be completely contained in Circle #2. There are two shapes that are on both lists: the square and the rhombus. These two shapes have all sides the same length *and* they have two pairs of parallel sides. These two shapes, the square and the rhombus, must be listed in the region that is in both circles, which is shaded above. All other shapes would be placed outside the circles.

Example 2

Based on the markings of each shape below, describe the shape using the most specific name possible.

a.   b.   c.

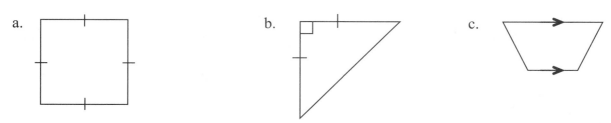

In Lesson 1.3.2 students created a Shapes Toolkit, that is, a resource page showing many different shapes. Using terms, definitions, and characteristics they had identified, students described the shapes on the resource page and added appropriate markings. Certain markings mean certain things in geometry.

The figure in part (a) appears to be a square, but based on its markings and the definition of a square, we cannot conclude that. The markings show that the sides of the quadrilateral are equal in length, but equal sides are not enough to make a square. To be a square it also needs four right angles. They angles in the drawing look like right angles, but maybe they are not quite 90°. They could be 89° and 91°, so without the appropriate markings or other information, we cannot assume the angles are right angles. This quadrilateral with four sides of equal length is called a **rhombus**.

Part (b) shows us two types of markings. The small box in the corner of the triangle tells us it is a right angle (measures 90°), so this is a right triangle. We know that the markings on the sides mean that the sides are the same length. A triangle with two sides that are the same length is called an isosceles triangle. Putting both of these facts together, we can label this figure an **isosceles right triangle**.

The arrowheads on the two sides of the quadrilateral of part (c) tells us that those sides are parallel. One pair of parallel sides makes this figure a **trapezoid**.

Example 3

Suppose we cut out the three shapes shown in the last example and place them into a bag. If we reach into the bag and randomly pull out a figure without looking, what is the probability that the shape is a triangle? What is the probability the shape has at least two sides of equal length? What is the probability that the shape has more than four sides?

To calculate probability, we count the number of ways a desired outcome can happen (successes) and divide that by the total number of possible outcomes. This explains why the probability of flipping tails with a fair coin is $\frac{1}{2}$. The number of ways we can get tails is one since there is only one tail, and the total number of outcomes is two (either heads or tails).

In our example, to calculate the probability that we pull out a triangle, we need to count the number of triangles in the bag (one) and divide that by the total number of shapes in the bag (three). This means the probability that we randomly pull out a triangle is $\frac{1}{3}$. To calculate the probability that we pull out a shape with at least two sides of equal length, we first count the number of shapes that would be a success (i.e., would fit this condition). The figures in parts (a) and (b) have at least two sides of equal length, so there are two ways to be successful. When we reach into the bag, there are three possible shapes we could pull out, so the total number of outcomes is three. Therefore, the probability of pulling out a shape with at least two sides of equal length is $\frac{2}{3}$. The probability that we reach into the bag and pull out a shape with more than four sides is calculated in the same way. We know that there are three outcomes (shapes), so three is the denominator. But how many ways can we be successful? Are there any shapes with more than four sides? No, so there are zero ways to be successful. Therefore the probability that we pull out a shape with more than four sides is $\frac{0}{3} = 0$.

Problems

Place the shapes from your Shapes Toolkit into the appropriate regions on the Venn diagram at right. The conditions that the shapes must meet to be placed in each circle are listed in each problem. Note: Create a new Venn diagram for each problem.

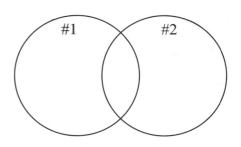

1. Circle #1: Has more than three sides; Circle #2: Has at least one pair of parallel sides.

2. Circle #1: Has fewer than four sides; Circle #2: Has at least two sides equal in length.

3. Circle #1: Has at least one curve; Circle #2: Has at least one obtuse angle.

Each shape below is missing markings. Add the correct markings so that the shape represents the term listed. Note: the pictures may not be drawn to scale.

4. A rectangle.

5. A scalene trapezoid.

6. An isosceles right triangle.

7. An equilateral quadrilateral.

Based on the markings, name the figure below with the most specific name. Note: The figures are not drawn to scale.

8.

9.

10.

11. On a spinner there are the numbers 1 through 36 along with 0 and 00. What is the probability that the spinner will stop on the number 17?

12. When Davis was finished with his checkerboard, he decided to turn it into a dartboard. If he is guaranteed to hit the board, but his dart will hit it randomly, what is the probability he will hit a shaded square?

Answers

1. Common to both circles and placed in the overlapping region are: square, rectangle, parallelogram, isosceles trapezoid, trapezoid, rhombus, and regular hexagon

    Only in Circle #1: quadrilateral, kite, and regular pentagon

    Only in Circle #2: none

    Outside of both circles: circle, scalene triangle, equilateral triangle, isosceles right triangle, isosceles triangle, and scalene right triangle

2. Common to both circles and placed in the overlapping region are: equilateral triangle, isosceles triangle, and isosceles right triangle

    Only in Circle #1: scalene triangle and scalene right triangle

    Only in Circle #2: square, rectangle, parallelogram, rhombus, kite, regular pentagon, isosceles trapezoid, and regular hexagon

    Outside of both circles: circle, quadrilateral, and trapezoid

3. There are no shapes with both characteristics, so there is nothing listed in the overlapping region.

    Only in Circle #1: circle

    Only in Circle #2: scalene triangle, parallelogram, isosceles trapezoid, trapezoid, quadrilateral, kite, rhombus, regular pentagon, and regular hexagon

    Outside of both circles: equilateral triangle, isosceles right triangle, isosceles triangle, scalene right triangle, rectangle, and square

4.

5.

6.

7.

8. A parallelogram

9. An isosceles triangle

10. An isosceles trapezoid

11. $P(\text{stop on } 17) = \frac{1}{38}$

12. $P(\text{hit a shaded square}) = \frac{1}{2}$

Applications of geometry in "everyday" settings often involve the measures of angles. In this chapter we begin our study of angle measurement. After describing angles and recognizing their characteristics, students complete an Angle Relationships Toolkit (Lesson 2.1.3 Resource Page). The toolkit lists some special angles and then students record important information about them. The list includes vertical angles (which are always equal in measure), straight angles (which measure 180°), corresponding angles, alternate interior angles, and same-side interior angles.

See the Math Notes boxes in Lessons 2.1.1 and 2.1.4 for more information about angle relationships.

Example 1

In each figure below, find the measures of angles a, b, and/or c. Justify your answers.

a.

b.

c.

d.

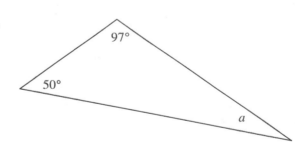

Each figure gives us information that enables us to find the measures of the other angles. In part (a), the little box at angle b tells us that angle b is a right angle, so $m\angle b = 90°$. The angle labeled c is a straight angle (it is opened wide enough to form a straight line) so $m\angle c = 180°$. To calculate $m\angle a$ we need to realize that $\angle a$ and the 72° angle are complementary which means together they sum to 90°. Therefore, $m\angle a + 72° = 90°$ which tells us that $m\angle a = 18°$.

In part (b) we will use two pieces of information, one about supplementary angles and one about vertical angles. First, $m\angle a$ and the 22° angle are supplementary because they form a straight angle (line), so the sum of their measures is 180°. Subtracting from 180° we find that $m\angle a = 158°$. Vertical angles are formed when two lines intersect. They are the two pairs of angles that are opposite (across from) each other where the lines cross. Their angle measures are always equal. Since the 22° angle and $\angle b$ are a pair of vertical angles, $m\angle b = 22°$. Similarly, $\angle a$ and $\angle c$ are vertical angles, and therefore equal, so $m\angle a = m\angle c = 158°$.

The figure in part (c) shows two parallel lines that are intersected by a transversal. When this happens we have several pairs of angles with equal measures. $\angle a$ and the 92° angle are called alternate interior angles, and since the lines are parallel (as indicated by the double arrows on the lines), these angles have equal measures. Therefore, $m\angle a = 92°$. There are several ways to calculate the remaining angles. One way is to realize that $\angle a$ and $\angle b$ are supplementary. Another uses the fact that $\angle b$ and the 92° angle are same-side interior angles, which makes them supplementary because the lines are parallel. Either way gives the same result: $m\angle b = 180° - 92° = 88°$. There is also more than one way to calculate $m\angle c$. We know that $\angle c$ and $\angle b$ are supplementary. Alternately, $\angle c$ and the 92° angle are corresponding angles, which are equal because the lines are parallel. A third way is to see that $\angle a$ and $\angle c$ are vertical angles. With any of these approaches, $m\angle c = 92°$.

Part (d) is a triangle. In class, students investigated the measures of the angles in a triangle. They found that the sum of the measures of the three angles always equals 180°. Knowing this, we can calculate $m\angle a$: $m\angle a + 50° + 97° = 180°$. Therefore, $m\angle a = 33°$.

Problems

Use the geometric properties and theorems you have learned to solve for x in each diagram and write the property or theorem you use in each case.

17.

18.

19.

20.

21.

22.

23.

24.

25.

26.

27.

28.

Use what you know about angle measures to find x, y, or z.

29.

30.

31.

32.

33.

34.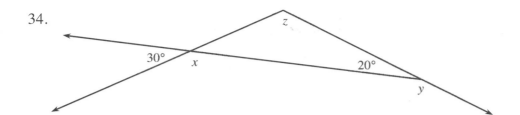

In Lesson 2.1.5 we used what we have learned about angle measures to create proofs by contradiction. (See the Math Notes box in Lesson 2.1.5.) Use this method of proof to justify each of your conclusions to problems 35 and 36 below.

35. Nik scored 40 points lower than Tess on their last math test. The scores could range from 0 to 100 points. Could Tess have scored a 30 on this test? Justify using a proof by contradiction.

36. Can a triangle have two right angles? Justify your answer with a proof by contradiction.

Answers

1. $x = 45°$

2. $x = 35°$

3. $x = 40°$

4. $x = 34°$

5. $x = 12.5°$

6. $x = 15°$

7. $x = 15°$

8. $x = 25°$

9. $x = 20°$

10. $x = 5°$

11. $x = 3°$

12. $x = 10\frac{2}{3}°$

13. $x = 7°$

14. $x = 2°$

15. $x = 7°$

16. $x = 25°$

17. $x = 81°$

18. $x = 7.5°$

19. $x = 9°$

20. $x = 7.5°$

21. $x = 7°$

22. $x = 15.6°$

23. $x = 26°$

24. $x = 2°$

25. $x = 40°$

26. $x = 65°$

27. $x = 7\frac{1}{6}°$

28. $x = 10°$

29. $(x + 5) + 4x = 180, x = 35°$

30. $(x + 13) + (2x + 7) + 5x = 180, x = 20°$

31. $(6x - 4) + (4x - 6) = 180, x = 19°, y = 110°$

32. $(x - 7) + (3x - 3) = 90, x = 25°, y = 90°$

33. $x = 28°, y = 52°, z = 80°$

34. $x = 150°, y = 160°, z = 130°$

35. If Tess scored 30 points, then Nik's score would be –10, which is impossible. So Tess cannot have a score of 30 points.

36. If a triangle has two right angles, then the measure of the third angle must be zero. However, this is impossible, so a triangle cannot have two right angles. OR: If a triangle has two 90° angles, the two sides that intersect with the side between them would be parallel and never meet to complete the triangle, as shown in the figure.

After measuring various angles, students look at measurement in more familiar situations, those of length and area on a flat surface. Students develop methods and formulas for calculating the areas of triangles, parallelograms, and trapezoids. They also find the areas of more complicated shapes by partitioning them into shapes for which they can use the basic area formulas. Students also learn how to determine the height of a figure with respect to a particular base.

See the Math Notes box in Lesson 2.2.4 for more information about area.

Example 1

In each figure, one side is labeled as the "base." For this "base," draw in a corresponding height.

a.
base

b.
base

c. base

d.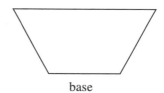
base

To find how tall a person is, we have them stand straight up and measure the distance from the highest point on their head straight down to the floor. We measure the height of figures in a similar way. One way to calculate the height is to visualize that the shape, with its base horizontal, needs to slide into a tunnel. How tall must the tunnel be so that the shape will slide into it? How tall the tunnel is equals the height of the shape. The height is perpendicular to the base (or a line that contains the base) from any of the shape's "highest" point(s). In class, students also used a 3×5 card to help them draw in the height.

a.   It is often easier to draw in the height of a figure when the base is horizontal, or the "bottom" of the figure. The height of the triangle at right is drawn from the highest point down to the base and forms a right angle with the base.

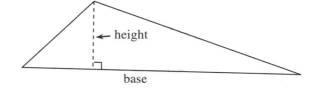

b. Even though the shape at right is not a triangle, it still has a height. In fact, the height can be drawn in any number of places from the side opposite the base. Three heights, all of equal length, are shown.

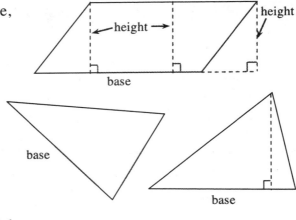

c. The base of the first triangle at right is different from the one in part (a) in that no side is horizontal or at the bottom. Rotate the shape, then draw the height as we did in part (a).

d. Shapes like the trapezoid at right or the parallelogram in part (b) have at least one pair of parallel sides. Because the base is always one of the parallel sides, we can draw several heights. The height at far right shows a situation where the height is drawn to a segment that contains the base segment.

Example 2

Find the area of each shape or its shaded region below. Be sure to include the appropriate units of measurement.

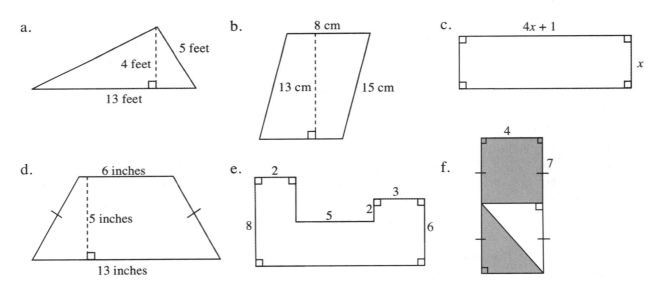

Students have the formulas for the areas of different shapes in their Area Toolkit (Lesson 2.2.4B Resource Page). For part (a), the area of a triangle is $A = \frac{1}{2}bh$, where b and h are perpendicular to each other. In this case, the base is 13 feet and the height is 4 feet. The side which is 5 feet is not a height because it does not meet the base at a right angle. Therefore, $A = \frac{1}{2}(13 \text{ feet})(4 \text{ feet}) = 26 \text{ feet}^2$. Area is measured in square units, while length (such as a perimeter) is measured in linear units, such as feet.

The figure in part (b) is a parallelogram and the area of a parallelogram is $A = bh$ where b and h are perpendicular. Therefore $A = (13 \text{ cm})(8 \text{ cm}) = 104$ square cm.

The figure in part (c) is a rectangle so the area is also $A = bh$, but in this case, we have variable expressions representing the lengths of the base and height. We still calculate the area in the same way. $A = (4x + 1)(x) = 4x^2 + x$ square units. Since we do not know in what units the lengths are measured, we say the area is just "square units."

Part (d) shows a trapezoid; the students found several different ways to calculate its area. The most common way is: $A = \frac{1}{2}(b_1 + b_2)h$ where b_1 is the upper base and b_2 is the lower base. As always, b and h must be perpendicular. The area is $A = \frac{1}{2}(6 \text{ in.} + 13 \text{ in.})5 \text{ in.} = 47.5$ square inches.

The figures shown in parts (e) and (f) are more complicated and one formula alone will not give us the area. In part (e), there are several ways to divide the figure into rectangles. One way is shown at right. The areas of the rectangles on either end are easy to find since the dimensions are labeled on the figure. The area of rectangle (1) is $A = (2)(8) = 16$ square units.

The area of rectangle (3) is $A = (3)(6) = 18$ square units. To find the area of rectangle (2), we know the length is 5 but we have to determine its height. The height is 2 shorter than 6, so the height is 4. Therefore, the area of rectangle (2) is $A = (5)(4) = 20$ square units. Now that we know the area of each rectangle, we can add them together to find the area of the entire figure: $A(\text{entire figure}) = 16 + 18 + 20 = 54$ square units.

In part (f), we are finding the area of the shaded region, and again, there are several ways to do this. One way is to see it as the sum of a rectangle and a triangle. Another way is to see the shaded figure as a tall rectangle with a triangle cut out of it. Either way will give the same answer.

Using the top method,
$A = 4(7) + \frac{1}{2}(4)(7) = 42$ square units.

The bottom method gives the same answer:
$A = 4(14) - \frac{1}{2}(4)(7) = 42$ square units.

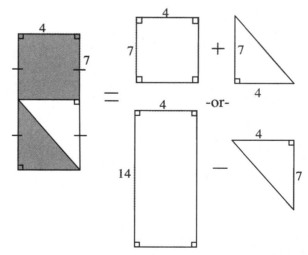

Problems

For each figure below, draw in a corresponding height for the labeled base.

1.

base

2.

base

3.

base

4.

base

Find the area of the following triangles, parallelograms and trapezoids. Pictures are not drawn to scale. Round answers to the nearest tenth.

5.

10
20

6.

36
5

7.

10
8
6

8.

6
5
4

9.

26
13
26

10.

15
7
15

11.

8
12
8
2

12.

4
20
16

13.

3
12
18

14.

3
9
4

15.

6
1.5
4
7

16.

$2\sqrt{10}$
10
8
6

17.

13
15
5
9

18.

23
5
$5\sqrt{2}$

19.

13
7
9

20.

6
4
4

Find the area of the shaded regions.

21.

22.

23.

24.

Find the area of each shape and/or shaded region. Be sure to include the appropriate units.

25.

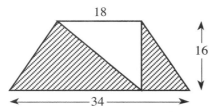

$3x + 5$

$2x$

26.

6.2 cm

27.

5

12

28.

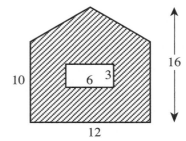

6 in.

4 in.

15.5 in.

29.

12 cm

2 cm   2 cm

3 cm

5 cm

7 cm   2.5 cm

9 cm

30.

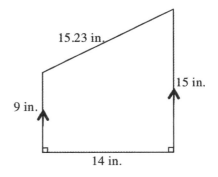

15.23 in.

15 in.

9 in.

14 in.

31.

32.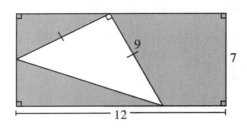

Find the area of each of the following figures. Assume that anything that looks like a right angle is a right angle.

33.

34.

35.

36.

37.

38.

39.

40.

41.

42.

Answers

1.

2.

3.

4.
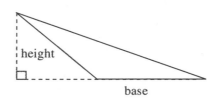

5. 100 sq. units   6. 90 sq. units   7. 24 sq. units   8. 15 sq. units

9. 338 sq. units   10. 105 sq. units   11. 93 sq. units   12. 309.8 sq. units

13. 126 sq. units   14. 19.5 sq. units   15. 36.3 sq. units   16. 54 sq. units

17. 84 sq. units   18. 115 sq. units   19. 110.8 sq. units   20. 7.9 sq. units

21. 1020 sq. units   22. 216 sq. units   23. 272 sq. units   24. 138 sq. units

25. $2x(3x+5)=6x^2+10x$ square units   26. $(6.2)^2 = 38.44$ square cm

27. $\frac{1}{2}(12)5 = 30$ square units   28. $(15.5)(4)=62$ square inches

29. $2(12)+7(6.5)+2(2.5)=74.5$ sq. cm   30. $9(14)+\frac{1}{2}(14)(6)=168$ square inches

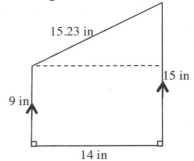

31. $\frac{1}{2}(7)(24)-(3)(5)=84-15=69$ sq. units

32. $(12)(7)-\frac{1}{2}(9)(9)=84-40.5=43.5$ sq. units

33. 42 units^2 34. 33 units^2 35. 85 units^2 36. 31 units^2 37. 36 units^2

38. 36 units^2 39. 36 units^2 40. 29.5 units^2 41. 46 units^2 42. 28 units^2

Using technology, students explore the Triangle Inequality, which determines the restrictions on the possible lengths of the third side of a triangle given the lengths of its other two sides. Using technology, students explore different ways to determine lengths of sides of triangles through calculation rather than measurement. The Triangle Inequality determines the restrictions on the possible lengths of the third side of a triangle given the lengths of its other two sides. Students use a method that reinforces the understanding of "square root" then use the method to apply the Pythagorean Theorem in right triangles.

See the Math Notes boxes in Lessons 2.3.1 and 2.3.2 for more information about right triangle vocabulary and the Pythagorean Theorem.

Example 1

The triangle at right does not have the lengths of its sides labeled. Can the sides have lengths of:

a.   3, 4, 5?   b.   8, 2, 12?

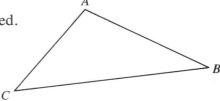

At first, students might think that the lengths of the sides of a triangle can be any three lengths, but that is not so. The Triangle Inequality says that the length of any side must be less than the sum of the lengths of the other two sides. For the triangle in part (a) to exist, all of these statements must be true:

$$5 \overset{?}{<} 3+4, \ 3 \overset{?}{<} 4+5, \text{ and } 4 \overset{?}{<} 5+3.$$

Since each of them is true, we could draw a triangle with sides of lengths 3, 4, and 5.

In part (b) we need to check if:

$$12 \overset{?}{<} 8+2, \ 8 \overset{?}{<} 2+12, \text{ and } 2 \overset{?}{<} 12+8.$$

In this case, only two of the three conditions are true, namely, the last two. The first inequality is not true so we cannot draw a triangle with side lengths of 8, 2, and 12. One way to make a convincing argument about this is to cut linguine or coffee stirrers to these lengths and see if you can put the pieces together at their endpoints to form a triangle.

Example 2

Use the Pythagorean Theorem to determine the value of x.

a.

b.

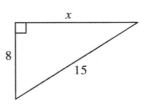

The two sides of a right triangle that form the right angle are called the **legs**, while the third side, the longest side of the triangle, is called the **hypotenuse**. The relationship between the lengths of the legs and the hypotenuse is shown at right.

The Pythagorean Theorem

$$(\text{leg})^2 + (\text{leg})^2 = (\text{hypotenuse})^2$$

In part (a), this gives us:

$$7^2 + 24^2 = x^2$$
$$49 + 576 = x^2$$
$$625 = x^2$$

To determine the value of x, use a calculator to find the square root of 625: $x = \sqrt{625}$, so $x = 25$.

Part (b) is a bit different in that the variable is not the hypotenuse. The solution is shown at right.

$$8^2 + x^2 = 15^2$$
$$64 + x^2 = 225$$
$$x^2 = 225 - 64$$
$$x^2 = 161$$
$$x = \sqrt{161}$$
$$x \approx 12.69$$

Problems

The triangle at right does not have any of the lengths of the sides labeled. Can the triangle have side lengths of:

1. $1, 2, 3$?

2. $7, 8, 9$?

3. $4.5, 2.5, 6$?

4. $9.5, 1.25, 11.75$?

5. A square has an area of 144 square feet. What is the length of one of its sides?

6. A square has an area of 484 square inches. What is the length of one of its sides?

7. A square has an area of 200 square cm. What is the length of one of its sides?

8. A square has an area of 169 square units. What is the perimeter of the square?

Use the Pythagorean Theorem to determine the value of x. Round answers to the nearest tenth.

9.
37
x
22

10.
96
20
x

11.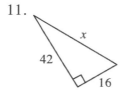
x
42
16

12.
x
83
46

13.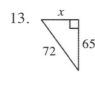
x
72
65

14.
x
16
22

15.
15
x
32

16.
x
16
38

17.
x
105
75

18.
30
125
x

Solve the following problems.

19. A 12 foot ladder is six feet from a wall. How high on the wall does the ladder touch?

20. A 15 foot ladder is five feet from a wall. How high on the wall does the ladder touch?

21. A 9 foot ladder is three feet from a wall. How high on the wall does the ladder touch?

22. A 12 foot ladder is three and a half feet from a wall. How high on the wall does the ladder touch?

23. A 6 foot ladder is one and a half feet from a wall. How high on the wall does the ladder touch?

24. Could 2, 3, and 6 represent the lengths of sides of a right angle triangle? Justify your answer.

25. Could 8, 12, and 13 represent the lengths of sides of a right triangle? Justify your answer.

26. Could 5, 12, and 13 represent the lengths of sides of a right triangle? Justify your answer.

27. Could 9, 12, and 15 represent the lengths of sides of a right triangle? Justify your answer.

28. Could 10, 15, and 20 represent the lengths of sides of a right triangle? Justify your answer.

Use the Pythagorean Theorem to find the value of x. When necessary, round your answer to the nearest hundredth.

29.

30.

31.

32.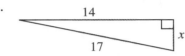

Answers

1. no	2. yes	3. yes
4. no	5. 12 feet	6. 22 inches
7. ≈ 14.14 cm	8. 52 units	9. $x = 27.7$ units
10. $x = 93.9$ units	11. $x = 44.9$ units	12. $x = 69.1$ units
13. $x = 31.0$ units	14. $x = 15.1$ units	15. $x = 35.3$ units
16. $x = 34.5$ units	17. $x = 73.5$ units	18. $x = 121.3$ units
19. 10.4 ft	20. 14.1 ft	21. 8.5 ft
22. 11.5 ft	23. 5.8 ft	24. no
25. no	26. yes	27. yes
28. no	29. $x \approx 23.85$ units	30. $x = 9$ units
31. $x \approx 5.66$ units	32. $x \approx 9.64$ units	

So far, students have measured, described, and transformed geometric shapes. In this chapter we focus on comparing geometric shapes. We begin by dilating shapes: enlarging them as one might on a copy machine. When students compare the original and enlarged shapes closely, they discover that the shape of the figure remains exactly the same (this means the angle measures of the enlarged figure are equal to those of the original figure), but the size changes (the lengths of the sides increase). Although the size changes, the lengths of the corresponding sides all have a constant ratio, known as the zoom factor, or ratio of similarity.

See the Math Notes boxes in Lessons 3.1.1, 3.1.2, 3.1.3, and 3.1.4 for more information about dilations and similar figures.

Example 1

Enlarge the figure at right from the origin by a factor of 3.

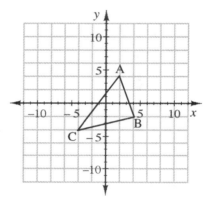

Students used rubber bands to create a dilation (enlargement) of several shapes. We can do this using a grid and slope triangles. Create a right triangle so that the segment from the origin to point A, (2, 4), is the hypotenuse, one leg lies on the positive *x*-axis, and the other connects point A to the endpoint of the leg at (0, 2). This triangle is called a slope triangle since it represents the slope of the hypotenuse from (0, 0) to vertex A. Add two more slope triangles exactly like this one along the line from (0, 0) to point A as shown in the figure at right. Using three triangles creates an enlargement by a factor of 3 and gives us the new point A′ at (6, 12). Repeat this process for the other two vertices, forming a new slope triangle for each vertex.

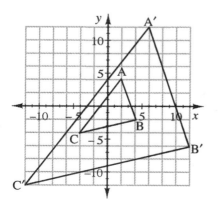

This will give us new points B′ at (12, −6) and C′ at (−12, −12). Connecting points A′, B′, and C′, we form a new triangle that is an enlargement of the original triangle by a factor of 3, as shown at left.

Example 2

The two quadrilaterals at right are similar. What parts are equal? Can you determine the lengths of any other sides?

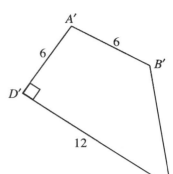

Similar figures have the same shape, but not the same size. Since the quadrilaterals are similar, we know that all the corresponding angles have the same measure. This means that $m\angle A = m\angle A'$, $m\angle B = m\angle B'$, $m\angle C = m\angle C'$, and $m\angle D = m\angle D'$. In addition, the corresponding sides are **proportional**, which means the ratio of corresponding sides is a constant. To find the ratio, we need to know the lengths of one pair of corresponding sides. From the picture we see that $\overline{AD}$ corresponds to $\overline{A'D'}$. Since these sides correspond, we can write $\frac{AD}{A'D'} = \frac{4}{6}$.

Therefore, the ratio of similarity is $\frac{4}{6}$, or $\frac{2}{3}$. We can use this value to find the lengths of other sides when we know at least one length of a corresponding pair of sides.

$$\frac{AB}{A'B'} = \frac{4}{6}$$
$$\frac{AB}{6} = \frac{4}{6}$$
$$AB = 4$$

$$\frac{BC}{B'C'} = \frac{4}{6}$$
$$\frac{8}{B'C'} = \frac{4}{6}$$
$$4B'C' = 48$$
$$B'C' = 12$$

$$\frac{CD}{C'D'} = \frac{4}{6}$$
$$\frac{CD}{12} = \frac{4}{6}$$
$$6CD = 48$$
$$CD = 8$$

Example 3

The pair of shapes at right is similar ($ABCDEF \sim UVWXYZ$). Label the second figure correctly to reflect the similarity statement.

Since similar figures have the same shape, just different sizes, this means that the corresponding angles have equal measure. When we write a similarity statement, we write the letters so that the corresponding angles match up. By the similarity statement, we must have $m\angle A = m\angle U$, $m\angle B = m\angle V$, $m\angle C = m\angle W$, $m\angle D = m\angle X$, $m\angle E = m\angle Y$, and $m\angle F = m\angle Z$.

The smaller figure is labeled at right. If it is difficult to tell which original angle corresponds to its enlargement or reduction, try rotating the figures so that they have the same orientation.

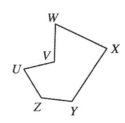

Problems

1. Copy the figure below onto graph paper and then enlarge it by a factor of 2.

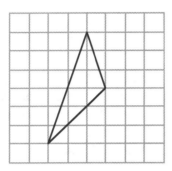

2. Create a figure similar to the one below with a zoom factor of 0.5.

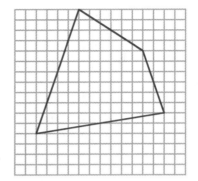

For each pair of similar figures below, find the ratio of similarity, for large:small.

3.

4.

5.

6.

7.

8.

For each pair of similar figures, state the ratio of similarity, then use it to find x.

9.

10.

11.

12.

13.

14.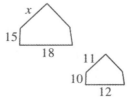

For problems 13 through 18, use the given information and the figure to find each length.

15. JM = 14, MK = 7, JN = 10   Find NL.

16. MN = 5, JN = 4, JL = 10   Find KL.

17. KL = 10, MK = 2, JM = 6   Find MN.

18. MN = 5, KL = 10, JN = 7   Find JL.

19. JN = 3, NL = 7, JM = 5   Find JK.

20. JK = 37, NL = 7, JM = 5   Find JN.

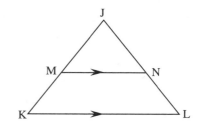

21. Standing 4 feet from a mirror lying on the flat ground, Palmer, whose eye height is 5 feet, 9 inches, can see the reflection of the top of a tree. He measures the mirror to be 24 feet from the tree. How tall is the tree?

22. The shadow of a statue is 20 feet long, while the shadow of a student is 4 ft long. If the student is 6 ft tall, how tall is the statue?

Each pair of figures below is similar. Use what you know about similarity to solve for x.

23.

24.

25.

26.

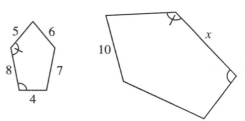

Solve for the missing lengths in the pairs of similar figures below.

27. $\triangle ABC \sim \triangle PQR$

28. $JKLM \sim WXYZ$

29. $STUV \sim MNOP$

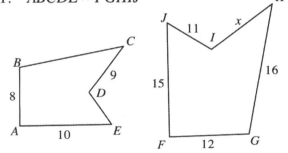

30. $\triangle DAV \sim \triangle ISW$

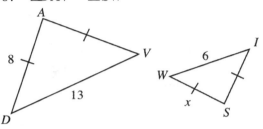

31. $ABCDE \sim FGHIJ$

32. $\triangle ABC \sim \triangle DBE$

Answers

1.

2.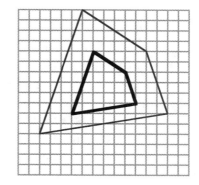

3. $\frac{4}{3}$

4. $\frac{5}{1}$

5. $\frac{2}{1}$

6. $\frac{24}{7}$

7. $\frac{6}{1}$

8. $\frac{15}{8}$

9. $\frac{7}{8}$; $x = 32$

10. $\frac{2}{1}$; $x = 72$

11. $\frac{1}{3}$; $x = 15$

12. $\frac{5}{6}$; $x = 15$

13. $\frac{4}{5}$; $x = 20$

14. $\frac{3}{2}$; $x = 16.5$

15. 5

16. 12.5

17. 7.5

18. 14

19. $16\frac{2}{3}$

20. $11\frac{25}{32}$

21. 34.5 ft

22. 30 ft

23. $x = 12$

24. $x = 9$

25. $x = 0.8$

26. $x = \frac{40}{3} \approx 13.33$

27. $x = 7.5$

28. $x = 1.25$

29. $x = 16$

30. $x \approx 3.69$

31. $x = 13.5$

32. $x = 12$

When two figures are related by a series of transformations (including dilations), they are similar. Another way to check for similarity is to measure all the angles and sides of two figures. In this section students develop conditions to shorten the process. These are the **AA Triangle Similarity Condition (AA~)**, the **SAS Triangle Similarity Condition (SAS~)**, and the **SSS Triangle Similarity Condition (SSS~)**. The first condition states that if two pairs of corresponding angles have equal measures, then the triangles are similar. The second condition states that if two pairs of corresponding side lengths have the same ratio, *and* their included angles have the same measure, then the triangles are similar. The third condition states that if all three pairs of corresponding side lengths have the same ratio, then the triangles are similar. Additionally, students found that if similar figures have a ratio of similarity of 1, then the shapes are **congruent**, that is, they have the same size and shape. Students used flowcharts in this section to help organize their information and make logical conclusions about similar triangles. Now students are able to use similar triangles to find side lengths, perimeters, heights, and other measurements.

See the Math Notes boxes in Lessons 3.2.1, 3.2.2, 3.2.4, and 3.2.5 for more information about similar triangles, congruent triangles, and writing flowcharts.

Example 1

Based on the given information, is each pair of triangles similar? If they are similar, write the similarity statement. Justify your answer completely.

a.

b.

c.

d.

e.

f.
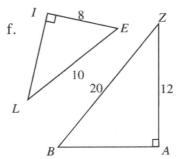

We will use the three similarity conditions to test whether or not the triangles are similar.

In part (a), we have the lengths of the three sides, so it makes sense to check whether the SSS~ holds true. Write the ratios of the corresponding side lengths and compare them to see if they are the same, as shown at right. Each ratio reduces to 3, so they are equal. Therefore, $\triangle TES \sim \triangle AWK$ by SSS ~.

$$\frac{ST}{KA} \overset{?}{=} \frac{TE}{AW} \overset{?}{=} \frac{ES}{WK}$$
$$\frac{9}{3} = \frac{18}{6} = \frac{12}{4}$$

The measurements given in part (b) suggest we look at SAS ~. $\angle A$ and $\angle R$ are the included angles. Since they are both right angles, they have equal measures. Now we need to check that the corresponding sides lengths have the same ratio, as shown at right.

$$\frac{LA}{ER} \overset{?}{=} \frac{AS}{RM}$$
$$\frac{8}{6} \overset{?}{=} \frac{6}{4}$$
$$\frac{4}{3} \neq \frac{3}{2}$$

Although the triangles display the SAS ~ pattern and the included angles have equal measures, the triangles are not similar because the corresponding side lengths do not have the same ratio.

In part (c), we are given the measures of two angles of each triangle, but not corresponding angles. $m\angle K = 55° = m\angle N$ which is one pair of corresponding angles. For AA~, we need two pairs of equal angles. If we use the fact that the measures of the three angles of a triangle add up to 180°, we can find the measures of $\angle O$ and $\angle E$ as shown at right. Now we see that all pairs of corresponding angles have equal measures, so $\triangle POK \sim \triangle EMN$ by AA~.

$$m\angle O = 180° - 53° - 55°$$
$$m\angle O = 72°$$

$$m\angle E = 180° - 55° - 72°$$
$$m\angle E = 53°$$

Part (d) shows the SAS~ pattern and we can see that the included angles have equal measures, $m\angle G = m\angle H$. We also need to have the ratio of the corresponding side lengths to be equal. Since the two fractions are equal (the second reduces to the first), the corresponding side lengths have the same ratio. Therefore, $\triangle YUG \sim \triangle IOH$ by SAS ~.

$$\frac{UG}{OH} \overset{?}{=} \frac{GY}{HI}$$
$$\frac{7}{12} = \frac{14}{24}$$

In part (e), we see that the included angles have equal measures, $m\angle B = m\angle N$. Since $\frac{45}{15} = \frac{9}{3} = \frac{3}{1}$, the corresponding sides are proportional. Therefore, $\triangle BOX \sim \triangle NTE$ by SAS ~.

In part (f), we only have one pair of angles that are equal (the right angles), but those angles are not between the sides with known lengths. However, we can find the lengths of the third sides by using the Pythagorean Theorem.

$$8^2 + (IL)^2 = 10^2 \qquad\qquad 12^2 + (AB)^2 = 20^2$$
$$64 + (IL)^2 = 100 \qquad\qquad 144 + (AB)^2 = 400$$
$$(IL)^2 = 36 \qquad\qquad (AB)^2 = 256$$
$$IL = 6 \qquad\qquad\qquad AB = 16$$

Now that we know all three sides, we can check to see if the triangles are similar by SSS ~. Since the ratios of the corresponding sides are the same, $\triangle ELI \sim \triangle BZA$ by SSS ~.

$$\frac{12}{6} \overset{?}{=} \frac{16}{8} \overset{?}{=} \frac{20}{10}$$
$$2 = 2 = 2$$

Example 2

In the figure at right, $\overline{AY} \parallel \overline{HP}$. Decide whether or not there are any similar triangles in the figure. Justify your answer with a flowchart.

Can you find the length of $\overline{AY}$? If so, find it. Justify your answer.

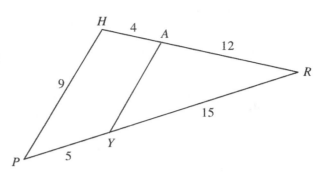

Recalling information we studied in earlier chapters, the parallel lines give us angles with equal measures. In this figure, we have two pairs of corresponding angles with equal measures: $m\angle PHR = m\angle YAR$ and $m\angle HPR = m\angle AYR$. Because two pairs of corresponding angles have equal measures, we can say the triangles are similar: $\triangle PHR \sim \triangle YAR$ by $AA \sim$. Since the triangles are similar, the lengths of corresponding sides are proportional (i.e., have the same ratio). This means we can write the solution at right.

$$\frac{RA}{RH} = \frac{AY}{HP}$$

$$\frac{12}{16} = \frac{AY}{9}$$

$$AY = \frac{9 \cdot 12}{16} = 6.75$$

We can justify this result with a flowchart as well. The flowchart at right organizes and states what is written above.

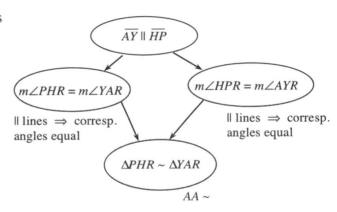

Problems

Each pair of figures below is similar. Write the correct similarity statements and solve for *x*.

1.

2.

3.

4.

Determine if each pair of triangles is similar. If they are similar, justify your answer.

5.

6.

7.

8.

9.

10.

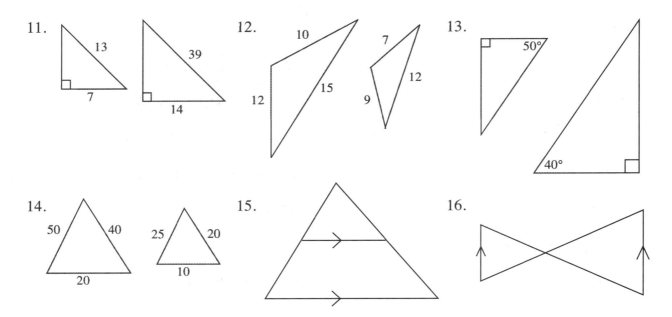

11. 12. 13.

14. 15. 16.

Decide if each pair of triangles is similar. If they are similar, write a correct similarity statement and justify your answer.

17. 18.

19. 20.

21. In the figure at right $\overline{AB} \parallel \overline{DE}$. Is $\triangle ABC$ similar to $\triangle EDC$? Use a flowchart to organize and justify your answer.

22. Standing four feet from a mirror resting on the flat ground, Palmer, whose eye height is 5 feet, 9 inches, can see the reflection of the top of a tree. He measures the mirror to be 24 feet from the tree. How tall is the tree? Draw a picture to help solve the problem.

Core Connections Geometry

Answers

1. $ABCDEF \sim UZYXWV$, $x = 3.75$

2. $RECT \sim NGLA$, $x = 8$

3. $\triangle IMS \sim \triangle RCH$, $x = 72$

4. $LACEY \sim ITHOM$, $x = 16.5$

5. AA ~

6. SSS ~

7. AA ~

8. SAS

9. not ~

10. not ~

11. SAS ~ or SSS ~

12. not ~

13. AA ~

14. SSS ~

15. AA ~

16. AA ~

17. $\triangle BOX \sim \triangle NCA$ by AA~

18. The triangles are not similar because the sides are not proportional.
$\frac{12}{15} = \frac{18}{22.5} = 0.8$, $\frac{10}{13} \approx 0.76$

19. $\triangle ALI \sim \triangle MES$ by SAS ~.

20. The triangles are not similar. On $\triangle SAM$, the 60° is included between the two given sides, but on $\triangle UEL$ the angle is not included.

21.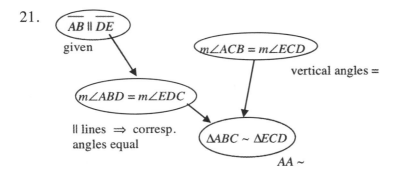

    Note: There is more than one way to solve this problem. Corresponding angles could have been used twice rather than mentioning vertical angles.

22. The figures at right show a sketch of the situation and how it translates into a diagram with triangles. $\triangle PFM \sim \triangle TRM$ by AA ~. The proportion is:

    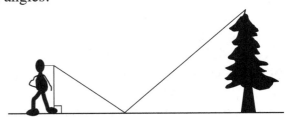

    $$\frac{x}{5.75} = \frac{24}{4}$$
    $$4x = 138$$
    $$x = 34.5$$

    Therefore, the tree is 34.5 feet tall.

    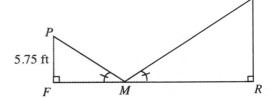

In the first section of Chapter 4, students consider different slope triangles for a given line or segment and notice that for each line, the slope remains constant no matter where they draw the slope triangle on that line or how large or small each slope triangle is. All the slope triangles on a given line are similar. These similar slope triangles allow students to write proportions to calculate lengths of sides and angle measures. This constant slope ratio is known as the "**tangent**" (trigonometric) relationship. Using the tangent button on their calculators, students are able to find measurements in application problems.

See the Math Notes boxes in Lessons 4.1.1, 4.1.2, and 4.1.4 for more information about slope angles and the tangent ratio.

Example 1

The line graphed at right passes through the origin. Draw in three different slope triangles for the line. For each triangle, what is the slope ratio, $\frac{\Delta y}{\Delta x}$? What is true about all three ratios?

Note: Δx (delta x) and Δy (delta y) are read "change in x" and "change in y."

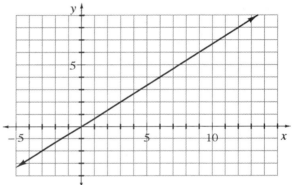

A slope triangle is a right triangle that has its hypotenuse on the line that contains it. This means that the two legs of the right triangle are parallel to the axes: one leg runs vertically, the other horizontally. There are infinitely many slope triangles that we can draw, but it is always easiest if we draw triangles that have their vertices on lattice points (that is, their vertices have integer coordinates). The length of the horizontal leg is Δx and the length of the vertical leg is Δy. At right are three possible slope triangles. For the smallest triangle, $\Delta x = 3$ (the length of the horizontal leg), and $\Delta y = 2$ (the length of the vertical leg). For the smallest triangle we have $\frac{\Delta y}{\Delta x} = \frac{2}{3}$.

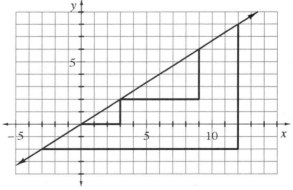

In the medium sized triangle, $\Delta x = 6$ and $\Delta y = 4$, which means $\frac{\Delta y}{\Delta x} = \frac{4}{6}$.

Lastly, the lengths on the largest triangle are $\Delta x = 15$ and $\Delta y = 10$, so $\frac{\Delta y}{\Delta x} = \frac{10}{15}$.

If we reduce the ratios to their lowest terms we find that the slope ratios, no matter where we draw the slope triangles for this line, are all equal. $\frac{\Delta y}{\Delta x} = \frac{2}{3} = \frac{4}{6} = \frac{10}{15}$

Students also discovered that different non-parallel lines do not have the same slope and slope ratio:the steeper the line, the larger the slope ratio, and the flatter the line, the smaller the slope ratio. In Lesson 4.1.2 students connect specific slope ratios to their related angles and record their findings in a Trig Table Toolkit (Lesson 4.1.2 Resource Page). They use this information to find missing side lengths and angle measures of right triangles. At the end of the section students use the tangent button on their calculators to find missing information in right triangles.

Example 2

Write an equation and use the tangent button on your calculator rather than your Trig Table Toolkit, to calculate the missing side length in each triangle.

a.

b.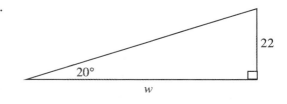

When using the tangent button on a calculator with these problems, you must be sure that the calculator is in degree mode and not radian mode. Student should be able to check this and fix it, if necessary. Since we found that the slope ratio depends on the angle, we can use the angle measure and the tangent button on the calculator to find unknown lengths of the triangle.

In part (a), we know that the tangent of the angle is the ratio $\frac{\text{opposite leg}}{\text{adjacent leg}} = \frac{\Delta y}{\Delta x}$. This allows us to write the equation at right and solve it. Using a calculator, the value of "tan 62°" is ≈ 1.88.

$$\tan 62° = \frac{q}{9.6} \left(\frac{\text{opposite leg}}{\text{adjacent leg}} \right)$$
$$9.6(\tan 62°) = q$$
$$q \approx (9.6)(1.88) \approx 18.048$$

In part (b) we will set up another equation similar to the previous one. This equation is slightly different from the one in our first example in that the variable is in the denominator rather than the numerator. This adds another step to the solution process. Some students might realize that they can rotate the triangle and use the 70° angle (which they would have to determine using the sum of the measures of the angles of the triangle) so that the unknown side length is in the numerator.

$$\tan 20° = \frac{22}{w}$$
$$w \tan 20° = 22$$
$$w = \frac{22}{\tan 20°}$$
$$w \approx 60.44$$

Example 3

Talula is standing 117 feet from the base of the Washington Monument in Washington, D.C. She uses her clinometer to measure the angle of elevation to the top of the monument to be 78°. If Talula's eye height is 5 feet, 3 inches, what is the height of the Washington Monument?

With all problems representing an everyday situation, the first step is the same: draw a picture of what the problem is describing. Here, we have Talula looking up at the top of a monument. We know how far away Talula is standing from the monument, we know her eye height, and we know the angle of elevation of her line of sight.

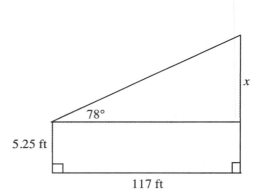

We translate this information from the picture to a diagram, as shown at right. On this diagram we include all the measurements we know. Then we write an equation using the tangent function and solve for x:

$$\tan 78° = \frac{x}{117}$$
$$117(\tan 78°) = x$$
$$x \approx 549.9 \text{ feet}$$

We add the "eye height" to the value of x to find the height of the Washington Monument:

$$549.9 + 5.25 \approx 555.15 \text{ feet}$$

Problems

For each line, draw in several slope triangles. Then calculate the slope ratios.

1.

2.

3.

4.

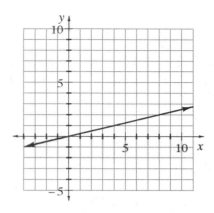

Calculate the measures of the variables. It may be helpful to rotate the triangle so that it resembles a slope triangle. If you write a tangent equation, use the tangent button on your calculator not your Trig Toolkit to solve. Note: Some calculations require the Pythagorean Theorem.

5.

6.

7.

8.

Careful!

9.

10.

11. A ladder makes a 75° angle with the wall it is leaning against. The base of the ladder is 5 feet from the wall. How high up the wall does the ladder reach?

12. Davis and Tess are 30 feet apart when Tess lets go of her helium-filled balloon, which rises straight up into the air. (It is a windless day.) After 4 seconds, Davis uses his clinometer to site the angle of elevation to the balloon at 35°. If Davis' eye height is 4 feet, 6 inches, what is the height of the balloon after 4 seconds?

Answers

1. In each case the slope ratio is $\frac{4}{1} = 4$.

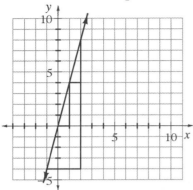

2. The slope ratio is $\frac{5}{5} = \frac{4}{4} = \frac{3}{3} = \frac{1}{1}$.

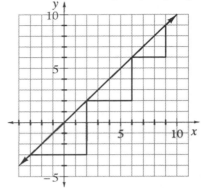

3. The slope ratio is $\frac{5}{3}$.

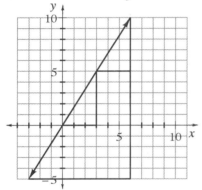

4. The slope ratio is $\frac{1}{4}$.

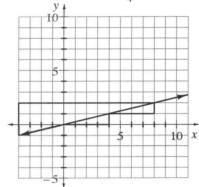

5. $\tan 28° = \frac{z}{14}$, $z \approx 7.44$

6. $\tan 70° = \frac{3.2}{m}$, $m \approx 2.75$, $\theta = 20°$

7. $\tan 33° = \frac{y}{210}$, $y \approx 136.38$, $\theta = 57°$

8. $c \approx 119.67$ (Pythagorean Theorem)

9. $\theta = 45°$, $x = 12.25$

10. $\tan 15° = \frac{w}{47}$, $w \approx 12.59$

11. $\tan 75° = \frac{h}{5}$; the ladder reaches about 18.66 feet up the wall.

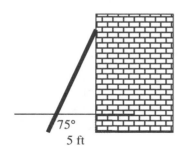

12. $\tan 35° = \frac{h}{30}$, $h \approx 21 + 4.5 \approx 25.5$; After 4 seconds the balloon is about 25.5 feet above the ground.

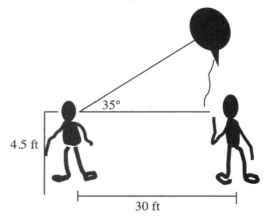

Although the definition of probability is simple, calculating a particular probability can sometimes be tricky. When calculating the probability of flipping a coin and having it come up tails, we can easily see that there are only two possibilities and one successful outcome. But what if neither the total number of outcomes nor the total number of successes is obvious? In this case, we need to have an accurate way to count the number of these events. In these lessons, we look at three models to do this: making a systematic list, making a tree diagram, and making an area model. Each different model has its strengths and weaknesses, and is more efficient in different situations.

See the Math Notes boxes in Lessons 4.2.3 and 4.2.4 for more information about calculating probabilities.

Example 1

As Ms. Dobby prepares the week's lunch menu for the students, she has certain rules that she must follow. She must have a meat dish and a vegetable at each lunch. She has four choices for meat: chicken, fish, beef, and pork. Her list of choices for vegetables is a bit larger: peas, carrots, broccoli, corn, potatoes, and beets. Considering just the meat and the vegetable, what is the probability that the first lunch she makes will have meat and a green vegetable?

To determine the probability of a lunch with meat and a green vegetable, we need to know how many different lunch menus are possible. Then we need to count how many of the lunch menus have meat and a green vegetable. To count all of the possible lunch menus, we will make a systematic list, pairing each meat with a vegetable in an organized way.

Chicken	Fish	Beef	Pork
Chicken and peas	Fish and peas	Beef and peas	Pork and peas
Chicken and carrots	Fish and carrots	Beef and carrots	Pork and carrots
Chicken and broccoli	Fish and broccoli	Beef and broccoli	Pork and broccoli
Chicken and corn	Fish and corn	Beef and corn	Pork and corn
Chicken and potatoes	Fish and potatoes	Beef and potatoes	Pork and potatoes
Chicken and beets	Fish and beets	Beef and beets	Pork and beets

From this list we can count the total number of lunch menus: 24. Then we count the number of lunch menus with meat and a green vegetable (peas or broccoli). There are 6 such menus. Therefore the probability of the first lunch menu having meat and a green vegetable is $\frac{6}{24} = \frac{1}{4}$.

Example 2

What is the probability of flipping a fair coin 4 times and have tails come up exactly two of those times?

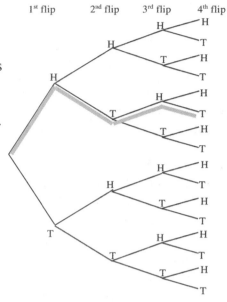

To solve this problem, we could make a systematic list as we did in the previous example, but there is another technique that works well for this type of problem. Since each flip gives us only two outcomes, we can organize this information in a tree diagram. The first flip has only two possibilities: heads (H) or tails (T). From each branch, we split again into H or T. We do this for each flip of the coin. The final number of branches at the end tells us the total number of outcomes. In this problem, there are 16 outcomes. We now count the number of "paths" along the branches that have exactly two Ts. One path consisting of HTHT is highlighted. The others are HHTT, HTTH, THHT, THTH, and TTHH, for a total of six paths. Thus the probability of flipping a coin four times and having T come up exactly two times is $\frac{6}{16} = \frac{3}{8}$.

Example 3

Romeo the rat is going to run through a maze to find a block of cheese. The floor plan of the maze is shown at right, with the cheese to be placed in either section A or section B. If every time Romeo comes to a split in the maze he is equally like to choose any path in front of him, what is the probability he ends up in section A?

To answer this question we will construct an area model to represent this situation. Using an area model is like turning the problem into a dartboard problem. It is easy to see what the probability of hitting the shaded portion on the dartboard at right is because the shaded portion makes up one-fourth of the board. Therefore the probability of hitting the shaded portion is $\frac{1}{4}$. What we want to do is turn the maze problem into a dartboard with the outcome we want (our success) represented by the shaded part.

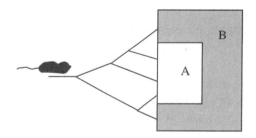

To begin, we start with a square dartboard. You can think of this as being a 1×1 square. When Romeo comes to the first branch in the maze, he has two choices: a top path and a bottom path. We represent this on the dartboard by splitting the board into two same sized (equally likely) pieces. Then consider what happens if Romeo chooses the bottom path first. If he chooses the bottom path, he comes to another split with two choices, each equally likely. On the area model (dartboard) we show this by splitting the bottom rectangle into two equally like sections, shown at right.

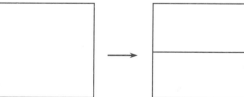

With one branch, Romeo will end up in section A; with the other branch he will end up in B. We indicate this by putting the letters in the regions representing these outcomes. Note: you can split the bottom rectangle in half with a "top" rectangle and a "bottom" rectangle as well. Since we are ultimately going to consider the area covered with an "A," it can be split in any way as long as the pieces are equal in size.

Now consider the top path. If Romeo takes the top path at the first split, he quickly comes to another split where again he has a choice of a top path or a bottom path. Once again we split the top rectangle into two same-sized rectangles since each path is equally likely. One box will represent the top path and one will represent the bottom. If Romeo takes the lower path, he will end up in section A. We indicate this by choosing one of the new regions as representing the lower path, and writing an A in that portion. If Romeo takes the upper path, he comes to another split, each equally likely. This means the last section of the dartboard that is not filled in needs to be cut into two equal parts, since each path is equally likely. One of the paths will lead directly to section A, the other to section B. Now we can fill in those letters as well.

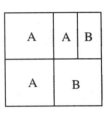

By looking at the dart board now, we can see that since A takes up more of the board, we would be more likely to hit section A. But to find the actual probability, we must determine how much area the sections marked with A take up. Recall that this is a 1×1 square. We can find the fraction of the area of each part. Remember: the key is that we divided regions up into equal parts. The length of each side of each rectangle is shown on the exterior of the square, while the area is written within the region. We want to know the probability of getting into section A, which is represented by the shaded portion of the dartboard. The area of the shaded region is:

$$A = \frac{1}{4} + \frac{1}{4} + \frac{1}{8}$$
$$= \frac{2}{8} + \frac{2}{8} + \frac{1}{8}$$
$$= \frac{5}{8}$$

Therefore the probability of Romeo wandering into section A is $\frac{5}{8}$. This means the probability that he wanders into section B is $\frac{3}{8}$ since the sum of both probabilities must be 1.

Problems

1. If Keisha has four favorite shirts (one blue, one green, one red, and one yellow) and two favorite pairs of pants (one black and one brown), how many different favorite outfits does she have? What is the best way to count this?

2. Each morning Aaron starts his day with either orange juice or apple juice followed by cereal, toast, or scrambled eggs. How many different morning meals are possible for Aaron?

3. Eliza likes to make daily events into games of chance. For instance, before she went to buy ice cream at the local ice cream parlor, she created two spinners. The first has her three favorite flavors while the second has "cone" and "dish." Eliza will order whatever comes up on the spinners. What is the probability that she will be eating tutti fruitti ice cream from a dish?

4. Barty is going to flip a coin three times. What is the probability that he will see *at least* two tails?

5. Mr. Fudge is going to roll two fair dice. What is the probability that the sum will be 4 or less?

6. Welcome to another new game show, "Spinning for Luck!" As a contestant, you will be spinning two wheels. The first wheel determines a possible dollar amount that you could win. The second wheel is the "multiplier." You will multiply the two results of your spin to determine the amount you will win. Unfortunately, you could *owe* money if your multiplier lands on –2! What is the probability that you could win $100 or more? What is the probability that you could owe $100 or more?

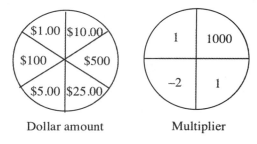

Dollar amount   Multiplier

For problems 7 through 10, a bag contains the figures shown below right. If you reach in and pull out a shape at random, what is the probability that you pull out:

7. A figure with at least one right angle?

8. A figure with an acute angle?

9. A shape with at least one pair of parallel sides?

10. A triangle?

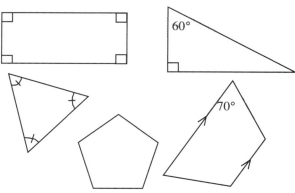

For each question that follows, use an area model or a tree diagram to compute the desired probability.

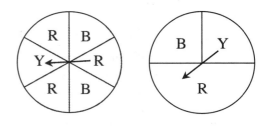

For problems 11-13 use the spinners at right.

11. If each spinner is spun once, what is the probability that both spinners show blue?

12. If each spinner is spun once, what is the probability that both spinners show the same color?

13. If each spinner is spun once, what is the probability of getting a red-blue combination?

14. A pencil box has three yellow pencils, one blue pencil, and two red pencils. There are also two red erasers and one blue. If you randomly choose one pencil and one eraser, what is the probability of getting the red-red combination?

15. Sally's mother has two bags of candy but she says that Sally can only have one piece. Bag #1 has 70% orange candies and 30% red candies. Bag #2 has 10% orange candies, 50% white candies, and 40% green candies. Sally's eyes are covered and she chooses one bag and pulls out one candy. What is the probability that she chooses an orange candy?

16. You roll a die and flip a coin. What is the probability of rolling a number less than 5 on the die and flipping tails on the coin?

17. A spinner is evenly divided into eight sections—three are red, three are white, and two are blue. If the spinner is spun twice, what is the probability of getting the same color twice?

18. You and your friend have just won a chance to collect a million dollars. You place the money in one room at right and then your friend has to randomly walk through the maze. In which room should you place the money so that your friend will have the best chance of finding the million dollars?

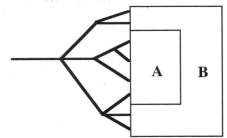

19. Find the probability of randomly entering each room in the maze shown at right.

   a.   P(A)   b.   P(B)   c.   P(C)

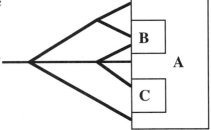

20. The weather forecast shows a 60% chance of rain. If it does not rain then there is an 80% chance of going to the beach. What is the probability of going to the beach

21. A baseball player gets a hit 40% of the time if the weather is nice but only 20% of the time if it is cold or windy. The weather forecast shows a 70% chance of being nice, 20% chance of being cold, and 10% chance of being windy. What is the probability of that the baseball player will get a hit?

22. If students have their assignments done on time there is an 80% chance of earning a good grade in the class. If the assignments are finished during class or late then there is only a 30% chance of earning a good grade in the class. If the assignments are not done at all then there is only a 5% chance of earning a good grade in the class. In a certain class, 50% of the students have the assignments completed on time, 40% finish during class, and 10% do not do their assignments. If a student is selected at random, what is the probability that student has a good grade?

Answers

1. Eight different outfits. A systematic list works best.

2. Six meals. A systematic list or tree diagram works.

3. $\frac{1}{3} \cdot \frac{1}{2} = \frac{1}{6}$

4. $\frac{1}{2}$ (See the tree diagram in Example 2.)

5. $\frac{10}{36} = \frac{5}{18}$

6. Winning $100 or more: $\frac{5}{12}$, owing $100 or more: $\frac{1}{12}$

7. $\frac{2}{5}$ 8. $\frac{3}{5}$ 9. $\frac{2}{5}$ 10. $\frac{2}{5}$

11. $\frac{1}{12}$ 12. $\frac{9}{24} = \frac{3}{8}$ 13. $\frac{7}{24}$ 14. $\frac{2}{9}$

15. $\frac{2}{5}$ 16. $\frac{1}{3}$ 17. $\frac{11}{32}$ 18. $P(B) = \frac{5}{9}$

19. $\frac{11}{18}, \frac{5}{18}, \frac{2}{18}$ 20. 0.32   21. 0.34   22. 0.525

Lesson 4.2.5 investigates expected value. Utilizing what students already know about probability, their study is extended, first through collecting data, and then by developing the mathematics behind the problem. Ultimately, students come up with a formula for calculating the expected value for each play of a game. Something to be careful of in this section: students sometimes think that the expected value must actually be one of the possible outcomes. It does not have to be. The expected value tells what is the average expected result for *one* play.

See the Math Notes box in Lesson 5.2.2 for more information about expected value.

Example 1

The spinner at right is divided into different sections, each assigned a different point value. The three smaller sections are congruent. If you were to spin the spinner 100 times, how many times would you expect to get each of the different point values? What is the expected value of this spinner?

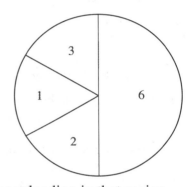

The size of each region is what determines the probability of the spinner landing in that region. Therefore the probability of landing on 6 points is $\frac{1}{2}$ because that region takes up half of the spinner. The other half of the circle is divided into three equal parts, each taking up $\frac{1}{6}$ of the whole spinner ($\frac{1}{3}$ of $\frac{1}{2}$). Now that we know the probabilities, we can determine how many times we would expect the values to come up. Since the probability of getting 6 points is $\frac{1}{2}$, we would expect that about half of the 100 spins would land on the 6, so 50 times. Similarly, since the probability of landing on 1 point (or 2 or 3) is $\frac{1}{6}$, would we expect about $\frac{1}{6}$ of the 100 spins to land on each of those, or about 16 or 17 times. If the total number of spins is 100, we can expect on average about 50 of them to be 6 points, $16\frac{2}{3}$ to be 1 point, $16\frac{2}{3}$ to be 2 points, and $16\frac{2}{3}$ to be 3 points. (Note: These are estimates, not exact or guaranteed.) Using these values, after 100 spins, the player would have about $50(6)+16\frac{2}{3}(1)+16\frac{2}{3}(2)+16\frac{2}{3}(3)=400$ points. If the player earns 400 points in 100 spins, then on average the player received 4 points per spin. So for any single spin, the expected value is 4 points. Note: 4 points is the expected value for this spinner, but it is NOT one of the possible outcomes.

Example 2

A 3×3 grid of nine congruent squares, each with a side length of 2 inches, is painted various colors. Six of the small squares are painted red while three are painted blue. For $1.00 a player can throw a dart at the grid. If the player hits a blue square, he is handed $2.00. Is this a fair game? Justify your answer.

The definition of a "fair" game is one in which the expected value is 0 because this means that, on average, the player is not guaranteed to win, and neither is the person running the game. If the expected value is 0, then winning or losing is just a matter of luck, and the game does not favor one side over the other. To determine if this game is fair we need to calculate its expected value.

Although we could go through a procedure similar to what we did in the last problem, there is a formula that is derived from that procedure that we can use. The expected value is found by summing the products of the amounts won and their probabilities. In this problem, each game costs $1.00 to play. If the dart lands on a red square, the player loses $1.00 (the value is -1). The probability of hitting a red square is $\frac{6}{9} = \frac{2}{3}$. However, if the player hits a blue square, the player receives $2.00, which wins only $1.00 (because he paid $1.00 for the dart). Based on the calculations at right, the expected value is $-\frac{1}{3}$. This tells us that on average the player can expect to lose $\frac{1}{3}$ of a dollar, or about $0.33, each turn. Therefore, this is not a fair game; it favors the person running the game.

$$E = \tfrac{2}{3}(-1.00) + \tfrac{1}{3}(1.00)$$
$$= -\tfrac{2}{3} + \tfrac{1}{3}$$
$$= -\tfrac{1}{3}$$

Example 3

In the previous problem, if we let Romeo run through the maze randomly 80 times, how many times would you expect him to end up in section A? In section B?

Now that we know the probability of Romeo wandering into each of the sections, we can figure out how many times we would *expect* him to reach each section. Since the probability of Romeo wandering into section A is $\frac{5}{8}$, we would expect Romeo to end up in section A 50 out of 80 times. Similarly, we would expect Romeo to wander into section B 30 times out of 80. This does not mean that Romeo will definitely wander into A 50 times out of 80. We are dealing with probabilities, not certainties, and this just gives us an idea of what to expect.

Problems

The spinners below have different point values assigned to the different regions. What is the expected value for each spinner? (Assume that regions that appear to be congruent, are congruent.)

1.

2.

3.

4.

5.

6.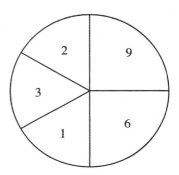

7. For $0.40 a player gets one dart to throw at a board that looks like the figure at right. The board is a square, measuring one foot along each side. The circle is centered and has a diameter of six inches. For each dart that lands in the interior of the circle, the players gets $0.75.
Is this game fair? Justify your answer.

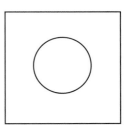

Answers

1. 2.5

2. 4

3. ≈ 3.7

4. 3

5. 5.5

6. 4.75

7. Not fair because the expected value is about −$1.25 .

We next introduce two more trigonometric ratios: sine and cosine. Both of them are used with acute angles of right triangles, just as the tangent ratio is. Using the diagram below:

$$\sin \theta = \frac{\text{opposite leg}}{\text{hypotenuse}} \qquad \cos \theta = \frac{\text{adjacent leg}}{\text{hypotenuse}}$$

and from Chapter 4: $\qquad \tan \theta = \dfrac{\text{opposite leg}}{\text{adjacent leg}}$

Note: If you decide to use the other acute angle in the triangle, then the names of the legs switch places. The opposite leg is always across the triangle from the acute angle you are using.

See the Math Notes boxes in Lessons 5.1.2 and 5.1.4.

Example 1

Use the sine ratio to find the length of the unknown side in each triangle below.

a.

b.

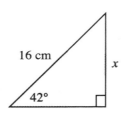

The sine of the angle is the ratio $\frac{\text{opposite leg}}{\text{hypotenuse}}$. For part (a) we will use the 78° as θ. From the 78° angle, we find which side of the triangle is the opposite leg and which side is the hypotenuse. The hypotenuse is always the longest side, and it is always opposite the right angle. In this case, it is 18. From the 78° angle, the opposite leg is the side labeled x. Now we can write the equation at right and solve it.

$$\sin 78° = \frac{x}{18} \quad \left(\frac{\text{opposite}}{\text{hypotenuse}} \right)$$
$$18 \sin 78° = x$$
$$x \approx 17.61 \text{ ft}$$

In part (b), from the 42° angle, the opposite leg is x and the hypotenuse is 16. We can write and solve the equation at right. Note: In most cases, it is most efficient to wait until the equation has been solved for x, then use your calculator to combine the values, as shown in these examples.

$$\sin 42° = \frac{x}{16}$$
$$16(\sin 42°) = x$$
$$x \approx 10.71 \text{ cm}$$

Example 2

Use the cosine ratio to find the length of the unknown side in each triangle below.

a.

b.

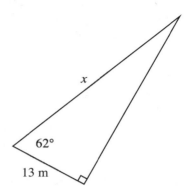

Just as before, we set up an equation using the cosine ratio, $\frac{\text{adjacent leg}}{\text{hypotenuse}}$. Remember that you can always rotate the page, or trace and rotate the triangle, if the figure's orientation is causing confusion. The key to solving these problems is recognizing which side is adjacent, which is opposite, and which is the hypotenuse. (See the box above Example 1 for this information.) For part (a), the angle is 25°, so we can write and solve the equation at right.

$$\cos 25° = \tfrac{x}{4} \; \left(\tfrac{\text{adjacent}}{\text{hypotenuse}} \right)$$
$$4(\cos 25°) = x$$
$$x \approx 3.63 \text{ yds}$$

In part (b), from the 62° angle, the adjacent leg is 13 and the hypotenuse is x. This time, our variable will be in the denominator. As we saw in earlier chapters, this will add one more step to the solution.

$$\cos 62° = \tfrac{13}{x}$$
$$x \cos 62° = 13$$
$$x = \tfrac{13}{\cos 62°} \approx 27.69 \text{ m}$$

Example 3

In each triangle below, use the inverse trigonometry buttons on your calculator to find the measure of the angle θ to the nearest hundredth.

a.

b.

c.

d.

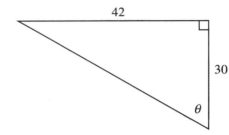

For each of these problems you must decide whether you will be using sine, cosine, or tangent to find the value of θ. In part (a), if we are standing at the angle θ, then 5 is the length of the opposite leg and 13 is the length of the hypotenuse. This tells us to use the sine ratio. For the best accuracy, enter the ratio, not its decimal approximation.

$$\sin \theta = \tfrac{5}{13}$$
$$\sin \theta \approx 0.385$$

To find the value of θ, find the button on the calculator that says $\sin^{-1}$. (Note: Calculator sequences shown are for most graphing calculators. Some calculators use a different order of keystrokes.) This is the "inverse sine" key, and when a ratio is entered, this button tells you the measure of the angle that has that sine ratio. Here we find $\sin^{-1} \tfrac{5}{13} \approx 22.62°$ by entering "2nd," "sin," (5 ÷ 13), "enter." Be sure to use parentheses as shown.

In part (b), 8 is the length of the adjacent leg and 12 is the length of the hypotenuse. This combination of sides fits the cosine ratio. We use the $\cos^{-1}$ button to find the measure of θ by entering the following sequence on the calculator: "2nd," "cos," (8 ÷ 12), "enter."

$$\cos \theta = \tfrac{8}{12}$$
$$\cos \theta \approx 0.667$$
$$\theta = \cos^{-1} \tfrac{8}{12}$$
$$\theta \approx 48.19°$$

In part (c), from θ, 7 is the length of the opposite leg and 14 is the length of the adjacent leg. These two sides fit the tangent ratio. As before, you need to find the $\tan^{-1}$ button on the calculator.

$$\tan \theta = \tfrac{7}{14} = 0.5$$
$$\tan \theta = 0.5$$
$$\theta = \tan^{-1} 0.5 \approx 26.57°$$

If we are standing at the angle θ in part (d), 42 is the length of the opposite leg while 30 is the length of the adjacent leg. We will use the tangent ratio to find the value of θ.

$$\tan \theta = \tfrac{42}{30} = 1.4$$
$$\tan \theta = 1.4$$
$$\theta = \tan^{-1} 1.4 \approx 54.46°$$

Example 4

Kennedy is standing on the end of a rope that is 40 feet long and threaded through a pulley. The rope is holding a large metal ball 18 feet above the floor. Kennedy slowly slides her feet closer to the pulley to lower the rod. When the rod hits the floor, what angle (θ) does the rope make with the floor where it is under her foot?

As always, we must draw a picture of this situation to determine what we must do. We start with a picture of the beginning situation, before Kennedy has started lowering the ball. The second picture shows the situation once the rod has reached the floor. We want to find the angle θ. You should see a right

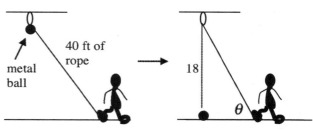

triangle emerging, made of the rope and the floor. The 40-foot rope makes up two sides of the triangle: 18 feet is the length of the leg opposite θ, and the rest of the rope, 22 feet of it, is the hypotenuse. With this information, draw one more picture. This one will show the simple triangle that represents this situation.

From θ, we have the lengths of the opposite leg and the hypotenuse. This tells us to use the sine ratio.

$$\sin \theta = \frac{18}{22}$$
$$\theta = \sin^{-1} \frac{18}{22}$$
$$\theta \approx 54.9°$$

Problems

Using the tangent, sine, and cosine buttons on your calculator, calculate the value of x to the nearest hundredth.

1.

2.

3.

4.

5.

6.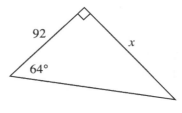

Using the $\sin^{-1}$, $\cos^{-1}$, and $\tan^{-1}$ buttons on your calculator, calculate the value of θ to the nearest hundredth.

7.

8.

9.

10.

11.

12.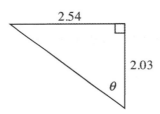

Use trigonometric ratios to solve for the variable in each figure below.

13.

14.

15.

16.

17.

18.

19.

20.

21.

22.

23.

24.

25.

26.

27.

28.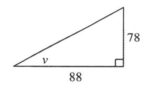

Draw a diagram and use trigonometric ratios to solve each of the following problems.

29. Juanito is flying a kite at the park and realizes that all 500 feet of string are out. Margie measures the angle of the string with the ground with her clinometer and finds it to be 42.5°. How high is Juanito's kite above the ground?

30. Nell's kite has a 350 foot string. When it is completely out, Ian measures the angle to be 47.5°. How far would Ian need to walk to be directly under the kite?

31. Mayfield High School's flagpole is 15 feet high. Using a clinometer, Tamara measured an angle of 11.3° to the top of the pole. Tamara is 62 inches tall. How far from the flagpole is Tamara standing?

32. Tamara took another sighting of the top of the flagpole from a different position. This time the angle is 58.4°. If everything else is the same, how far from the flagpole is Tamara standing?

33. Standing 140 feet from the base of a building, Alejandro uses his clinometer to site the top of the building. The reading on his clinometer is 42°. If his eyes are 6 feet above the ground, how tall is the building?

34. An 18 foot ladder rests against a wall. The base of the ladder is 8 feet from the wall. What angle does the ladder make with the ground?

Answers

1. $\tan 40° = \frac{18}{x}$, $x \approx 21.45$

2. $\cos 49° = \frac{x}{75}$, $x \approx 49.20$

3. $\sin 36° = \frac{x}{10}$, $x \approx 5.88$

4. $\sin 19° = \frac{27}{x}$ or $\cos 71° = \frac{27}{x}$, $x \approx 82.93$

5. $\cos 45° = \frac{x}{11.31}$, $x \approx 8.00$

6. $\tan 64° = \frac{x}{92}$, $x \approx 188.63$

7. $\sin \theta = \frac{13}{19}$, $\theta \approx 43.17°$

8. $\tan \theta = \frac{24}{8}$, $\theta \approx 71.57°$

9. $\cos \theta = \frac{53}{68}$, $\theta \approx 38.79°$

10. $\tan \theta = \frac{34}{23}$, $\theta \approx 55.92°$

11. $\sin \theta = \frac{35}{58}$, $\theta \approx 37.12°$

12. $\tan \theta = \frac{2.54}{2.03}$, $\theta \approx 51.37°$

13. $h = 15 \sin 38° \approx 9.235$

14. $h = 8 \sin 26° \approx 3.507$

15. $x = 23 \cos 49° \approx 15.089$

16. $x = 37 \cos 41° \approx 27.924$

17. $y = 38 \tan 15° \approx 10.182$

18. $y = 43 \tan 55° \approx 61.4104$

19. $z = \frac{15}{\sin 38°} \approx 24.364$

20. $z = \frac{18}{\sin 52°} \approx 22.8423$

21. $w = \frac{23}{\cos 38°} \approx 29.1874$

22. $w = \frac{15}{\cos 38°} \approx 19.0353$

23. $x = \frac{38}{\tan 15°} \approx 141.818$

24. $x = \frac{91}{\tan 29°} \approx 164.168$

25. $x = \tan^{-1} \frac{5}{7} \approx 35.5377°$

26. $u = \tan^{-1} \frac{7}{9} \approx 37.875°$

27. $y = \tan^{-1} \frac{12}{18} \approx 33.690°$

28. $y = \tan^{-1} \frac{78}{88} \approx 41.5526°$

29.

    $\sin 42.5 = \frac{h}{500}$
    $h = 500 \sin 42.5° \approx 337.795$ ft

30.

    $\cos 47.5° = \frac{d}{350}$
    $d = 350 \cos 47.5° \approx 236.46$ ft

31.

    15 feet = 180 inches,
    $180'' - 62'' = 118'' = h$
    $x \approx 590.5$ inches or 49.2 ft.

32.

    $h = 118''$, $\tan 58.4° = \frac{118''}{x}$,
    $x \tan 58.4 = 118''$, $x = \frac{118''}{\tan 58.4°}$
    $x \approx 72.59$ inches or 6.05 ft.

33. $\tan 42° = \frac{h}{140}$, $h \approx 132$ feet

34. $\cos \theta = \frac{8}{18}$, $\theta \approx 63.61°$

There are two special right triangles that occur often in mathematics: the 30°-60°-90° triangle and the 45°-45°-90° triangle. By AA~, all 30°-60°-90° triangles are similar to each other, and all 45°-45°-90° triangles are similar to each other. Consequently, for each type of triangle, the sides are proportional. The sides of these triangles follow these patterns.

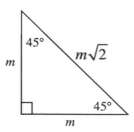

Another short cut in recognizing side lengths of right triangles are Pythagorean Triples. The lengths 3, 4, and 5 are sides of a right triangle (Note: You can verify this with the Pythagorean Theorem) and the sides of all triangles similar to the 3-4-5 triangle will have sides that form Pythagorean Triples (6-8-10, 9-12-15, etc). Another common Pythagorean Triple is 5-12-13.

See the Math Notes boxes in Lessons 5.2.1 and 5.3.1.

Example 1

The triangles below are either a 30°-60°-90° triangle or a 45°-45°-90° triangle. Decide which it is and find the lengths of the other two sides based on the pattern for that type of triangle.

a.

b.

c.

d.

e.

f.

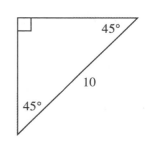

In part (a), this is a 30°-60°-90° triangle, so its sides will fit the pattern for such a triangle. The pattern tells us that the hypotenuse is twice the length of the short leg. Since the short leg has a length of 6, the hypotenuse has a length of 12. The long leg is the length of the short leg times $\sqrt{3}$, so the long leg has a length of $6\sqrt{3}$.

In part (b), we have a 30°-60°-90° triangle again, but this time we know the length of the hypotenuse. Following the pattern, this means the length of the short leg is half the hypotenuse: 7. As before, we multiply the length of the short leg by $\sqrt{3}$ to get the length of the long leg: $7\sqrt{3}$.

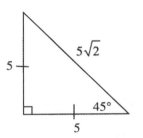

The triangle in part (c) is a 45°-45°-90° triangle. The missing angle is also 45°; you can verify this by remembering the sum of the angles of a triangle is 180°. The legs of a 45°-45°-90° triangle are equal in length (it is isosceles) so the length of the missing leg is also 5. To find the length of the hypotenuse, we multiply the leg's length by $\sqrt{2}$. Therefore the hypotenuse has length $5\sqrt{2}$.

We have another 30°-60°-90° triangle in part (d). This time we are given the length of the long leg. To find the short leg, we *divide* the length of the long leg by $\sqrt{3}$. Therefore, the length of the short leg is 8. To find the length of the hypotenuse, we double the length of the short leg, so the hypotenuse is 16.

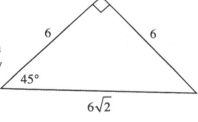

The triangle in part (e) is a 45°-45°-90° triangle, and we are given the length of the hypotenuse. To find the length of the legs (which are equal in length), we will divide the length of the hypotenuse by $\sqrt{2}$. Therefore, each leg has length 6.

If you understand what was done in each of the previous parts, part (f) is no different from the rest. This is a 45°-45°-90° triangle, and we are given the length of the hypotenuse. However, we are used to seeing the hypotenuse of a 45°-45°-90° triangle with a $\sqrt{2}$ attached to it. In the last part when we were given the length of the hypotenuse, we divided by $\sqrt{2}$ to find the length of the legs, and this time we do the same thing.

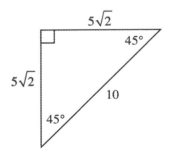

$$\frac{10}{\sqrt{2}} = \frac{10}{\sqrt{2}} \cdot \frac{\sqrt{2}}{\sqrt{2}} = \frac{10\sqrt{2}}{2} = 5\sqrt{2}$$

Note: Multiplying by $\frac{\sqrt{2}}{\sqrt{2}}$ is called rationalizing the denominator. It is a technique to remove the radical from the denominator.

Core Connections Geometry

Example 2

Use what you know about Pythagorean Triples and similar triangles to fill in the missing lengths of sides below.

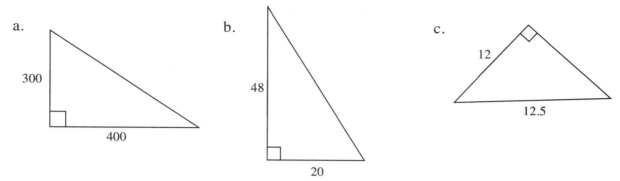

There are a few common Pythagorean Triples that students should recognize; 3–4–5, 5–12–13, 8–15–17, and 7–24–25 are the most common. If you forget about a particular triple or do not recognize one, you can always find the unknown side by using the Pythagorean Theorem if two of the sides are given. In part (a), this is a multiple of a 3–4–5 triangle. Therefore the length of the hypotenuse is 500. In part (b), we might notice that each leg has a length that is a multiply of four. Knowing this, we can rewrite them as $48 = 4(12)$, and $20 = (4)(5)$. This is a multiple of a 5–12–13 triangle, the multiplier being 4. Therefore, the length of the hypotenuse is $4(13) = 52$. In part (c), do not let the decimal bother you. In fact, since we are working with Pythagorean Triples and their multiples, double both sides to create a similar triangle. This eliminates the decimal. That makes the leg 24 and the hypotenuse 25. Now we recognize the triple as 7–24–25. Since the multiple is 0.5, the length of the other leg is 3.5.

Problems

Identify the special triangle relationships. Then solve for $x, y,$ or both.

1.

2.

3.

4.

5.

6.

7.

8.

9.

10.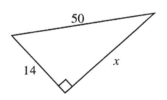

Answers

1. $x = 8\sqrt{3}, y = 8$

2. $x = y = 8$

3. $x = 13$

4. $y = 800$

5. $x = 6, y = 6\sqrt{2}$

6. $x = y = \frac{12}{\sqrt{2}} = 6\sqrt{2}$

7. $x = 11\sqrt{3}, y = 22$

8. $x = 45, y = 22.5$

9. $x = 34$

10. $x = 48$

Students have several tools for finding parts of right triangles, including the Pythagorean Theorem, the tangent ratio, the sine ratio, and the cosine ratio. These relationships only work, however, with *right* triangles. What if the triangle is not a right triangle? Can we still calculate lengths and angles with trigonometry from certain pieces of information? Yes, by using two laws, the Law of Sines and the Law of Cosines that state:

Law of Sines

$$\frac{\sin(m\angle A)}{a} = \frac{\sin(m\angle B)}{b}$$

$$\frac{\sin(m\angle B)}{b} = \frac{\sin(m\angle C)}{c}$$

$$\frac{\sin(m\angle A)}{a} = \frac{\sin(m\angle C)}{c}$$

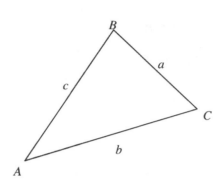

Law of Cosines

$$c^2 = a^2 + b^2 - 2ab\cos C \qquad b^2 = a^2 + c^2 - 2ac\cos B \qquad a^2 = b^2 + c^2 - 2bc\cos A$$

See the Math Notes boxes in Lessons 5.3.2 and 5.3.3.

Example 1

Using the Law of Sines, calculate the value of x.

a.

b.

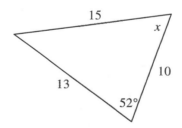

We will set up ratios that are equal according to the Law of Sines. The ratio compares the sine of the measure of an angle to the length of the side opposite that angle. In part (a), 21 is the length of the side opposite the 35° angle, while x is the length of the side opposite the 65° angle. The proportion is shown at right. To solve the proportion, we cross multiply, and solve for x. We can use the Law of Sines to find the measure of an angle as well. In part (b), we again write a proportion using the Law of Sines.

$$\frac{\sin 35°}{21} = \frac{\sin 65°}{x}$$

$$x\sin 35° = 21\sin 65°$$

$$x = \frac{21\sin 65°}{\sin 35°}$$

$$x \approx 33.18$$

$$\frac{\sin x}{13} = \frac{\sin 52°}{15}$$

$$15\sin x = 13\sin 52°$$

$$\sin x = \frac{13\sin 52°}{15}$$

$$\sin^{-1} x = 13\sin 52° \div 15$$

$$x \approx 43.07°$$

Example 2

Use the Law of Cosines to solve for x in the triangles below.

a.

b.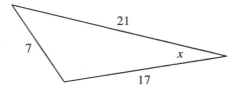

The Law of Cosines does not use ratios, as the Law of Sines does. Rather, it uses a formula somewhat similar to the Pythagorean Theorem. For part (a) the formula gives us the equation and solution shown below.

$$x^2 = 6^2 + 9^2 - 2(6)(9)\cos 93°$$
$$x^2 \approx 36 + 81 - 108(-0.052)$$
$$x^2 \approx 117 + 5.612$$
$$x^2 \approx 122.612$$
$$x \approx 11.07$$

Just as with the Law of Sines, we can use the Law of Cosines to find the measures of angles as well as side lengths. In part (b) we will use the Law of Cosines to find the measure of angle x. From the law we can write the equation and solution shown below.

$$7^2 = 17^2 + 21^2 - 2(17)(21)\cos x$$
$$49 = 289 + 441 - 714\cos x$$
$$49 = 730 - 714\cos x$$
$$-681 = -714\cos x$$
$$\frac{-681}{-714} = \cos x$$
$$x \approx 17.49° \text{ (using } \cos^{-1} x)$$

Example 3

Marisa's, June's, and Daniel's houses form a triangle. The distance between June's and Daniel's houses is 1.2 km. Standing at June's house, the angle formed by looking out to Daniel's house and then to Marisa's house is 63°. Standing at Daniel's house, the angle formed by looking out to June's house and then to Marisa's house is 75°. What is the distance between all of the houses?

The trigonometry ratios and laws are very powerful tools in real world situations. As with any application, the first step is to draw a picture of the situation. We know the three homes form a triangle, so we start with that. We already know one distance: the distance from June's house to Daniel's house. We write 1.2 as the length of the side from D to J. We also know that $m\angle J = 63°$ and $m\angle D = 75°$, and can figure out that $m\angle M = 42°$. We are trying to find the lengths of $\overline{DM}$ and $\overline{MJ}$. To do this, we will use the Law of Sines.

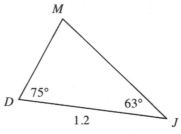

MJ: $\quad \frac{\sin 75°}{MJ} = \frac{\sin 42°}{1.2}$

$\quad 1.2\sin 75° = (MJ)\sin 42°$

$\quad \frac{1.2\sin 75°}{\sin 42°} = MJ$

$\quad MJ \approx 1.73$ km

DM: $\quad \frac{\sin 63°}{DM} = \frac{\sin 42°}{1.2}$

$\quad 1.2\sin 63° = (DM)\sin 42°$

$\quad \frac{1.2\sin 63°}{\sin 42°} = DM$

$\quad DM \approx 1.60$ km

Therefore the distances between the homes are: From Marisa's to Daniel's: 1.6 km, from Marisa's to June's: 1.73 km, and from Daniel's to June's: 1.2 km.

Core Connections Geometry

Problems

Use the tools you have for triangles to solve for x, y, or θ. Round all answers to the nearest hundredth.

1.

2.

3.

4.

5.

6.

7.

8.

9.

10.
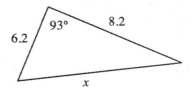

Use the Law of Sines or the Law of Cosines to find the required part of the triangle.

11.

12.

13.

14.

15.

16.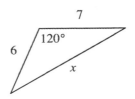

Draw and label a triangle similar to the one in the examples. Use the given information to find the required part(s).

17. $m\angle A = 40°, m\angle B = 88°, a = 15$.
    Find b.

18. $m\angle B = 75°, a = 13, c = 14$.
    Find b.

19. $m\angle B = 50°, m\angle C = 60°, b = 9$.
    Find a.

20. $m\angle A = 62°, m\angle C = 28°, c = 24$.
    Find a.

21. $m\angle A = 51°, c = 8, b = 12$.
    Find a.

22. $m\angle B = 34°, a = 4, b = 3$.
    Find c.

23. $a = 9, b = 12, c = 15$.
    Find $m\angle B$.

24. $m\angle B = 96°, m\angle A = 32°, a = 6$.
    Find c.

25. $m\angle C = 18°, m\angle B = 54°, b = 18$.
    Find c.

26. $a = 15, b = 12, c = 14$.
    Find $m\angle C$.

27. $m\angle C = 76°, a = 39. B = 19$.
    Find c.

28. $m\angle A = 30°, m\angle C = 60°, a = 8$.
    Find b.

29. $a = 34, b = 38, c = 31$.
    Find $m\angle B$.

30. $a = 8, b = 16, c = 7$.
    Find $m\angle C$.

31. $m\angle C = 84°, m\angle B = 23°, c = 11$.
    Find b.

32. $m\angle A = 36°, m\angle B = 68°, b = 8$.
    Find a and c.

33. $m\angle B = 40°, b = 4$, and $c = 6$.
    Find $a, m\angle A$, and $m\angle C$.

34. $a = 2, b = 3, c = 4$.
    Find $m\angle A, m\angle B$, and $m\angle C$.

35. Marco wants to cut a sheet of plywood to fit over the top of his triangular sandbox. One angle measures 38°, and it is between sides with lengths 14 feet and 18 feet. What is the length of the third side?

36. From the planet Xentar, Dweeble can see the stars Quazam and Plibit. The angle between these two sites is 22°. Dweeble knows that Quazam and Plibit are 93,000,000 miles apart. He also knows that when standing on Plibit, the angle made from Quazam to Xentar is 39°. How far is Xentar from Quazam?

Core Connections Geometry

Answers

1. $x \approx 13.00, y = 107°$

2. $x \approx 16.60$

3. $x \approx 3.42$

4. $x \approx 8.41, y = 34°$

5. $\theta \approx 16.15°$

6. $\theta \approx 37.26°$

7. $\theta \approx 32.39°$

8. $x \approx 9.08$

9. $\theta \approx 81.61°$

10. $x \approx 10.54$

11. 24.49

12. 22.6

13. 4.0

14. 83.3°

15. 17.15

16. 11.3

17. 23.32

18. 16.46

19. 11.04

20. 45.14

21. 9.34

22. 5.32 or 1.32

23. 53.13°

24. 8.92

25. 6.88

26. 61.28°

27. 39.03

28. 16

29. 71.38°

30. no triangle

31. 4.32

32. 5.07, 8.37

33. 5.66, 65.4°, 74.6°

34. 28.96°, 46.57°, 104.45°

35. ≈ 11.08 feet

36. $\approx 156,235,361$ miles

Sometimes the information we know about sides and angle of a triangle is not enough to make one unique triangle. Sometimes a triangle may not even exist, as we saw when we studied the Triangle Inequality. When a triangle formed is not unique (that is, more than one triangle can be made with the given conditions) we call this **triangle ambiguity**. This happens when we are given two sides and an angle *not* between the two sides, known as SSA.

Example 1

In $\triangle ABC$, $m\angle A = 50°$, $AB = 12$, and $BC = 10$. Can you make a unique triangle? If so, find all the angle measures and side lengths for $\triangle ABC$. If not, show more than one triangle that meets these conditions.

As with many problems, we will first make a sketch of what the problem is describing.

Once we label the figure, we see that the information displays the SSA pattern mentioned above. It does seem as if this triangle can exist. First try to find the length of side AC. To do this we will use the Law of Cosines.

$$10^2 = 12^2 + x^2 - 2(12)(x)\cos 50°$$
$$100 = 144 + x^2 - 24x\cos 50°$$
$$100 \approx 144 + x^2 - 15.43x$$
$$x^2 - 15.43x + 44 \approx 0$$

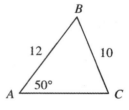

Now we have a type of equation we have not seen when solving this sort of problem. This is a quadratic equation. To solve it, we will use the Quadratic Formula (see the Math Notes box in Lesson 4.2.1). Recall that a quadratic equation may have two different solutions. We will use the formula and see what happens.

$$x^2 - 15.43x + 44 = 0$$
$$x = \frac{15.43 \pm \sqrt{15.43^2 - 4(1)(44)}}{2(1)}$$
$$\approx \frac{15.43 \pm \sqrt{238.08 - 176}}{2}$$
$$\approx \frac{15.43 \pm \sqrt{62.08}}{2}$$
$$\approx \frac{15.43 \pm 7.88}{2}$$
$$x \approx \frac{15.43 + 7.88}{2} \text{ or } x \approx \frac{15.43 - 7.88}{2}$$
$$x \approx 11.65 \text{ or } x \approx 3.78$$

Both of these answers are positive numbers, and could be lengths of sides of a triangle. So what happened? If we drew the triangle to scale, we would notice that although we drew the triangle with $\angle C$ acute, it does not have to be. Nothing in the information given says to draw the triangle this way. In fact, since there are no conditions on $m\angle B$ the side $\overline{BC}$ can swing as if it is on a hinge

 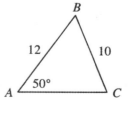

at $\angle B$. As you move $\overline{BC}$ along $\overline{AC}$, $\overline{BC}$ can intersect $\overline{AC}$ at two different places and still be 10 units long. In one arrangement, $\angle C$ is fairly small, while in the second arrangement, $\angle C$ is larger. (Note: The triangle formed with the two possible arrangements (the light grey triangle) is isosceles. From that you can conclude that the two possibilities for $\angle C$ are supplementary.)

Problems

Partial information is given about a triangle in each problem below. Solve for the remaining parts of the triangle, explain why a triangle does not exist, or explain why there is more than one possible triangle.

1. In $\triangle ABC$, $\angle A = 32°$, $AB = 20$, and $BC = 12$.

2. In $\triangle XYZ$, $\angle Z = 84°$, $XZ = 6$, and $YZ = 9$.

3. In $\triangle ABC$, $m\angle A = m\angle B = 45°$ and $AB = 7$.

4. In $\triangle PQR$, $PQ = 15$, $\angle R = 28°$, and $PR = 23$.

5. In $\triangle XYZ$, $\angle X = 59°$, $XY = 18$, and $YZ = 10$.

6. In $\triangle PQR$, $\angle P = 54°$, $\angle R = 36°$, and $PQ = 6$.

Answers

1. Two triangles: AC ≈ 22.58, $m\angle B \approx 85.34°$, $m\angle C \approx 62.66°$ or $AC \approx 11.35$, $m\angle B \approx 30.04°$, $m\angle C \approx 117.96°$

2. One triangle: $XY \approx 10.28$, $m\angle X \approx 60.54°$, $m\angle Y \approx 35.46°$

3. One triangle: $m\angle C \approx 90°$, $BC = AC = \frac{7\sqrt{2}}{2} \approx 4.95$

4. Two triangles: $QR \approx 30.725$, $m\angle Q \approx 46.04°$, $m\angle P \approx 105.96°$, or $QR \approx 9.895$, $m\angle Q \approx 133.96°$, $m\angle P \approx 18.04°$

5. No triangle exists. Note: If you use Law of Cosines, you will have a negative number under the square root sign. This means there are no real number solutions.

6. One triangle: $m\angle Q = 90°$, $QR \approx 8.26$, $PR \approx 10.21$

Two triangles are congruent if there is a sequence of rigid transformations that carry one onto the other. Two triangles are also congruent if they are similar figures with a ratio of similarity of 1, that is $\frac{1}{1}$. One way to prove triangles congruent is to prove they are similar first, and then prove that the ratio of similarity is 1. In these lessons, students find short cuts that enable them to prove triangles congruent in fewer steps, by developing five triangle congruence conjectures. They are SSS ≅, ASA ≅, AAS ≅, SAS ≅, and HL ≅, illustrated below.

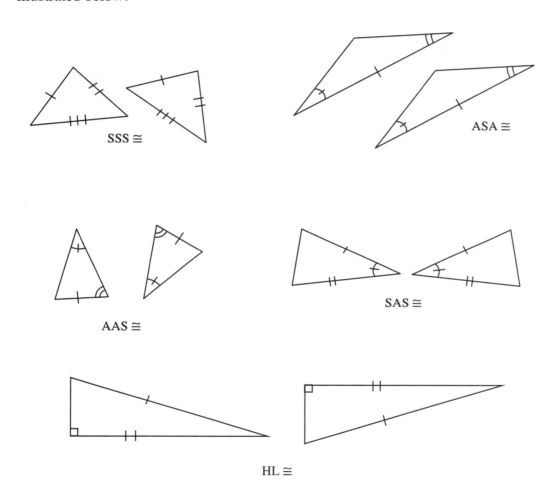

Note: "S" stands for "side" and "A" stands for "angle." HL ≅ is only used with right triangles. The "H" stands for "hypotenuse" and the "L" stands for "leg." The pattern appears to be "SSA" but this arrangement is NOT one of our conjectures, since it is only true for right triangles.

See the Math Notes boxes in Lessons 6.1.1 and 6.1.4.

Example 1

Use your triangle congruence conjectures to decide whether or not each pair of triangles must be congruent. Base each decision on the markings, not on appearances. Justify each answer.

a.

b.

c.

d.

e.

f.

In part (a), the triangles are congruent by the SAS ≅ conjecture. The triangles are also congruent in part (b), this time by the SSS ≅ conjecture. In part (c), the triangles are congruent by the AAS ≅ conjecture. Part (d) shows a pair of triangles that are not necessarily congruent. The first triangle displays an ASA arrangement, while the second triangle displays an AAS arrangement. The triangles could still be congruent, but based on the markings, we cannot conclude that they definitely are congruent. The triangles in part (e) are right triangles and the markings fit the HL ≅ conjecture. Lastly, in part (f), the triangles are congruent by the ASA ≅ conjecture.

Example 2

Using the information given in the diagrams below, decide if any triangles are congruent, similar but not congruent, or not similar. If you claim the triangles are congruent or similar, create a flow chart justifying your answer.

a.

b.

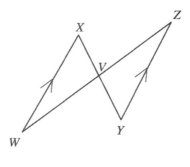

In part (a), $\triangle ABD \cong \triangle CBD$ by the SAS $\cong$ conjecture. Note: If you only see "SA," observe that $\overline{BD}$ is congruent to itself. The **Reflexive Property** justifies stating that something is equal or congruent to itself.

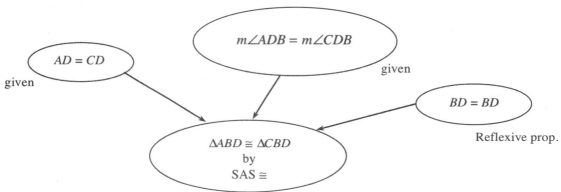

In part (b), $\triangle WXV \sim \triangle ZYV$ by the AA $\sim$ conjecture. The triangles are not necessarily congruent; they could be congruent, but since we only have information about angles, we cannot conclude anything else.

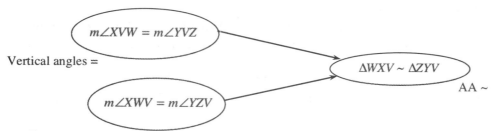

There is more than one way to justify the answer to part (b). There is another pair of alternate interior angles ($\angle WXV$ and $\angle ZYV$) that are equal that we could have used rather than the vertical angles, or we could have used them along with the vertical angles.

Problems

Briefly explain if each of the following pairs of triangles are congruent or not. If so, state the triangle congruence conjecture that supports your conclusion.

1.

2.

3.

4.

5.

6.

7.

8.

9.

10.

11.

12.

13.

14.

15.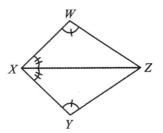

Use your triangle congruence conjectures to decide whether or not each pair of triangles must be congruent. Base your decision on the markings, not on appearances. Justify your answer.

16.

17.

18.

19.

20.

21.
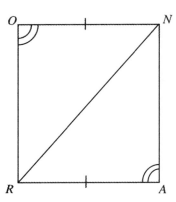

Using the information given in each diagram below, decide if any triangles are congruent, similar but not congruent, or not similar. If you claim the triangles are congruent or similar, create a flowchart justifying your answer.

22.

23.

24.

25.
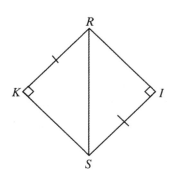

In each diagram below, are any triangles congruent? If so, prove it. (Note: Justify some using flowcharts and some by writing two-column proofs.)

26.

27.

28.

29.

30.

31.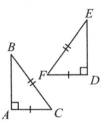

Complete a proof for each problem below in the style of your choice.

32. Given: $\overline{TR}$ and $\overline{MN}$ bisect each other.
    Prove: $\triangle NTP \cong \triangle MRP$

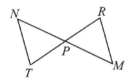

33. Given: $\overline{CD}$ bisects $\angle ACB$; $\angle 1 \cong \angle 2$.
    Prove: $\triangle CDA \cong \triangle CDB$

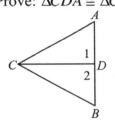

34. Given: $\overline{AB} \parallel \overline{CD}$, $\angle B \cong \angle D$, $\overline{AB} \cong \overline{CD}$
    Prove: $\triangle ABF \cong \triangle CDE$

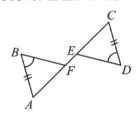

35. Given: $\overline{PG} \cong \overline{SG}$, $\overline{TP} \cong \overline{TS}$
    Prove: $\triangle TPG \cong \triangle TSG$

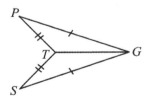

36. Given: $\overline{OE} \perp \overline{MP}$, $\overline{OE}$ bisects $\angle MOP$
    Prove: $\triangle MOE \cong \triangle POE$

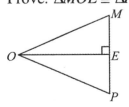

37. Given: $\overline{AD} \parallel \overline{BC}$, $\overline{DC} \parallel \overline{BA}$
    Prove: $\triangle ADB \cong \triangle CBD$

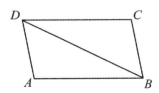

38. Given: $\overline{AC}$ bisects $\overline{DE}$, $\angle A \cong \angle C$
    Prove: $\triangle ADB \cong \triangle CEB$

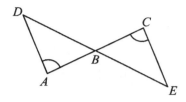

39. Given: $\overline{PQ} \perp \overline{RS}$, $\angle R \cong \angle S$
    Prove: $\triangle PQR \cong \triangle PQS$

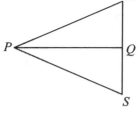

40. Given: $\angle S \cong \angle R$, $\overline{PQ}$ bisects $\angle SQR$
    Prove: $\triangle SPQ \cong \triangle RPQ$

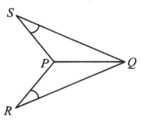

41. Given: $\overline{TU} \cong \overline{GY}$, $\overline{KY} \parallel \overline{HU}$, $\overline{KT} \perp \overline{TG}$, $\overline{HG} \perp \overline{TG}$. Prove: $\angle K \cong \angle H$

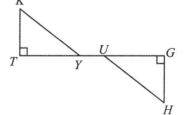

42. Given: $\overline{MQ} \parallel \overline{WL}$, $\overline{MQ} \cong \overline{WL}$
    Prove: $\overline{ML} \parallel \overline{WQ}$

Consider the diagram at right.

43. Is $\triangle BCD \cong \triangle EDC$? Prove it!

44. Is $\overline{AB} \cong \overline{DC}$? Prove it!

45. Is $\overline{AB} \cong \overline{ED}$? Prove it!

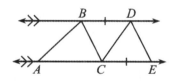

Answers

1. $\triangle ABC \cong \triangle DEF$ by ASA.

2. $\triangle GIH \cong \triangle LJK$ by SAS.

3. $\triangle PNM \cong \triangle PNO$ by SSS.

4. $\overline{QS} \cong \overline{QS}$, so $\triangle QRS \cong \triangle QTS$ by HL.

5. The triangles are not necessarily congruent.

6. $\triangle ABC \cong \triangle DFE$ by ASA or AAS.

7. $\overline{GI} \cong \overline{GI}$, so $\triangle GHI \cong \triangle IJG$ by SSS.

8. Alternate interior angles = used twice, so $\triangle KLN \cong \triangle NMK$ by ASA.

9. Vertical angles $\cong$ at 0, so $\triangle POQ \cong \triangle ROS$ by SAS.

10. Vertical angles and/or alternate interior angles =, so $\triangle TUX \cong \triangle VWX$ by ASA.

11. No, the length of each hypotenuse is different.

12. Pythagorean Theorem, so $\triangle EGH \cong \triangle IHG$ by SSS.

13. Sum of angles of triangle = 180°, but since the equal angles do not correspond, the triangles are not congruent.

14. $AF + FC = FC + CD$, so $\triangle ABC \cong \triangle DEF$ by SSS.

15. $\overline{XZ} \cong \overline{XZ}$, so $\triangle WXZ \cong \triangle YXZ$ by AAS.

16. $\triangle ABC \cong \triangle EDC$ by AAS $\cong$

17. $\triangle PQS \cong \triangle PRS$ by AAS $\cong$, with $\overline{PS} \cong \overline{PS}$ by the Reflexive Property.

18. $\triangle VXW \cong \triangle ZXY$ by ASA $\cong$, with $\angle VXW \cong \angle ZXY$ because vertical angles are $\cong$.

19. $\triangle TEA \cong \triangle SAE$ by SSS $\cong$, with $\overline{EA} \cong \overline{EA}$ by the Reflexive Property.

20. $\triangle KLB \cong \triangle EBL$ by HL $\cong$, with $\overline{BL} \cong \overline{BL}$ by the Reflexive Property.

21. Not necessarily congruent.

22. $\triangle DAV \sim \triangle ISV$ by SAS $\sim$

$$\frac{DV}{IV} = \frac{AV}{SV}$$

Equal markings

$m\angle DVA = m\angle IVS$

$\triangle DAV \sim \triangle ISV$

Vert. angles =

SAS~

23. $\triangle LUN$ and $\triangle HTC$ are not necessarily similar based on the markings.

24. $\triangle SAP \sim \triangle SJE$ by AA~.

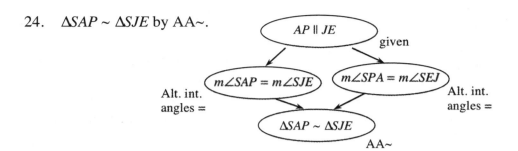

25. $\triangle KRS \cong \triangle ISR$ by HL $\cong$

26. Yes

27. Yes

28. Yes

29. Yes

30. Not necessarily. Counterexample:

31. Yes

32. $\overline{NP} \cong \overline{MP}$ and $\overline{TP} \cong \overline{RP}$ by definition of bisector. $\angle NPT \cong \angle MPR$ because vertical angles are equal. So, $\triangle NTP \cong \triangle MRP$ by SAS.

33. $\angle ACD \cong \angle BCD$ by definition of angle bisector. $\overline{CD} \cong \overline{CD}$ by reflexive so $\triangle CDA \cong \triangle CDB$ by ASA.

34. $\angle A \cong \angle C$ since alternate interior angles of parallel lines congruent so $\triangle ABF \cong \triangle CDE$ by ASA.

35. $\overline{TG} \cong \overline{TG}$ by reflexive so $\Delta TPG \cong \Delta TSG$ by SSS.

36. $\angle MEO \cong \angle PEO$ because perpendicular lines form $\cong$ right angles $\angle MOE \cong \angle POE$ by angle bisector and $\overline{OE} \cong \overline{OE}$ by reflexive. So, $\Delta MOE \cong \Delta POE$ by ASA.

37. $\angle CDB \cong \angle ABD$ and $\angle ADB \cong \angle CBD$ since parallel lines give congruent alternate interior angles. $\overline{DB} \cong \overline{DB}$ by reflexive so $\Delta ADB \cong \Delta CBD$ by ASA.

38. $\overline{DB} \cong \overline{EB}$ by definition of bisector. $\angle DBA \cong \angle EBC$ since vertical angles are congruent. So $\Delta ADB \cong \Delta CEB$ by AAS.

39. $\angle RQP \cong \angle SQP$ since perpendicular lines form congruent right angles. $\overline{PQ} \cong \overline{PQ}$ by reflexive so $\Delta PQR \cong \Delta PQS$ by AAS.

40. $\angle SQP \cong \angle RQP$ by angle bisector and $\overline{PQ} \cong \overline{PQ}$ by reflexive, so $\Delta SPQ \cong \Delta RPQ$ by AAS.

41. $\angle KYT \cong \angle HUG$ because parallel lines form congruent alternate exterior angles. $TY + YU = YU + GU$ so $TY \cong GU$ by subtraction. $\angle T \cong \angle G$ since perpendicular lines form congruent right angles. So $\Delta KTY \cong \Delta HGU$ by ASA. Therefore, $\angle K \cong \angle H$ since $\cong$ triangles have congruent parts.

42. $\angle MQL \cong \angle WLQ$ since parallel lines form congruent alternate interior angles. $\overline{QL} \cong \overline{QL}$ by reflexive so $\Delta MQL \cong \Delta WLQ$ by SAS so $\angle WQL \cong \angle MLQ$ since congruent triangles have congruent parts. So $\overline{ML} \parallel \overline{WQ}$ since congruent alternate interior angles are formed by parallel lines.

43. Yes

44. Not necessarily.

45. Not necessarily.

A conditional statement is a sentence in the "If – then" form. "If all sides are equal in length, then a triangle is equilateral" is an example of a conditional statement. We can abbreviate conditional statements by creating an **arrow diagram**. When the clause after the "if" in a conditional statement exchanges places with the clause after the "then," the new statement is called the **converse** of the original. If the conditional statement is true, the converse is not necessarily true, and vice versa.

See the Math Notes box in Lesson 6.1.5.

Example 1

Read each conditional statement below. Rewrite it as an arrow diagram, and state whether or not it is true. Then write the converse of the statement, and state whether or not the converse is true.

a.   If a triangle is equilateral, then it is equiangular.

b.   If $x = 4$, then $x^2 = 16$.

c.   If $ABCD$ is a square, then $ABCD$ is a parallelogram.

The arrow diagram for part (a) is not much shorter than the original statement: Δ is equilateral $\Rightarrow$ Δ is equiangular

The converse is: If a triangle is equiangular, then it is equilateral. This statement and the original conditional statement are both true.

In part (b), the conditional statement is true and the arrow diagram is: $x = 4 \Rightarrow x^2 = 16$.

The converse of this statement, "If $x^2 = 16$, then $x = 4$," is not necessarily true because x could equal –4.

In part (c), the arrow diagram is: $ABCD$ is a square $\Rightarrow$ $ABCD$ is a parallelogram.

This statement is true, but the converse, "If $ABCD$ is a parallelogram, then $ABCD$ is a square," is not necessarily true. It could be a parallelogram or a rectangle.

Problems

Rewrite each conditional statement below as an arrow diagram and state whether or not it is true. Then write the converse of the statement and state whether or not the converse is true.

1.   If an angle is a straight angle, then the angle measures 180°.

2.   If a triangle is a right triangle, then the sum of the squares of the lengths of the legs is equal to the square of the length of the hypotenuse.

3.   If the measures of two angles of one triangle are equal to the measures of two angles of another triangle, then the measures of the third angles are also equal.

4.   If one angle of a quadrilateral is a right angle, then the quadrilateral is a rectangle.

5.   If two angles of a triangle have equal measures, then the two sides of the triangle opposite those angles have equal length.

Answers

1.   Conditional: True

                    180°

Converse: If an angle measures 180°, then it is a straight angle. True.

2.   Conditional: True

$a^2 + b^2 = c^2$

Converse: If the sum of the squares of the lengths of the legs is equal to the square of the length of the hypotenuse, then the triangle is a right triangle. True.

3.   Conditional: True

Converse: If the measures of one pair of corresponding angles of two triangles are equal, then the measures of the two other pairs of corresponding angles are also equal. False.

4.   Conditional: False

→   *ABCD* is a rectangle

Converse: If a quadrilateral is a rectangle, then one angle is a right angle. True, in fact, all four angles are right angles.

5.   Conditional: True

Converse: If two sides of a triangle are equal in length, then the two angles opposite those sides are equal in measure. True.

The remaining sections of Chapter 6 are devoted to doing big problems. Students solve problems that involve many of the topics that they have studied so far, giving them the chance to connect the ideas and information as well as extend it to new situations.

Example 1

To frame a doorway, strips of wood surround the opening creating a "frame." If the doorway's dimensions are 30 inches by 80 inches and the strips of wood are $2\frac{1}{2}$ inches wide, how much wood is needed to frame the doorway and how should it be cut? Assume that the strips will be assembled as shown in the figure at right and that they are sold in 8' lengths.

Cutting two pieces of wood 80 inches long, and one piece 30 inches long will not enable us to make a frame for the doorway. The inside edges of the strips of wood will have those measurements, but the outside dimensions of the wood are longer.

The wood strips will meet at a 45° angle at the corners of the doorframe. Looking at the corner carefully (as shown at right) we see two 45°-45°-90° triangles in the corner. The lengths AD and CD are both $2\frac{1}{2}$ inches, since they are the width of the strips of wood.

Since a 45°-45°-90° triangle is isosceles, this means AB and BC are also $2\frac{1}{2}$ inches in length. Therefore, we need two strips that are $82\frac{1}{2}$ inches long ($80 + 2\frac{1}{2}$), and one strip that is 35 inches long ($30 + 2\frac{1}{2} + 2\frac{1}{2}$), because each end must extend the width of the vertical strip). Since the strips come in 8-foot lengths, we would need to buy three of them. Two will be cut at a 45° angle, with the outsides edge $82\frac{1}{2}$ inches long and the inside edges 80 inches long. The third piece has two 45° angle cuts. The outside length is 35 inches while the inside length is 30 inches.

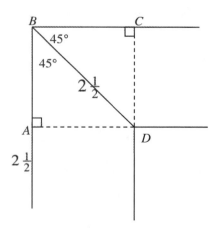

Example 2

A friend offers to play a new game with you, using the spinner shown at right. Your friend says that you can choose to be player 1 or 2. On each turn, you will spin the spinner twice. If the letters are the same, player 1 gets a point. If the letters are different, then player 2 gets the point. Which player would you choose to be? Justify your answer.

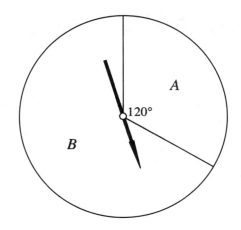

To help us decide which player to be, we will create an area model to represent the probabilities. On the area model, the left edge represents the two outcomes from the first spin; the top edge represents the outcomes from the second spin. On the first spin, there are two possible outcomes, A and B, which are *not* equally likely. In fact, the probability of B occurring is $P(B) = \frac{2}{3}$, while the probability of A occurring is $P(A) = \frac{1}{3}$. This is true for the first spin and the second spin. We divide the area model according to these probabilities, and fill in the possible outcomes.

Player 1 receives a point when the letters are the same for both spins. This outcome is represented by the shaded squares. Player 2 receives the point when the letters are different. By multiplying the dimensions of each region, the areas are expressed as ninths and we see that:

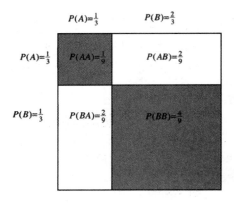

$$P(1 \text{ gets a point}) = \tfrac{1}{9} + \tfrac{4}{9} = \tfrac{5}{9}$$

and

$$P(2 \text{ gets a point}) = \tfrac{2}{9} + \tfrac{2}{9} = \tfrac{4}{9}$$

Since the probability that player 1 will win a point is greater than the probability that player 2 will, we should choose to be player 1.

Problems

1. On graph paper, plot the points $A(3, -4)$, $B(8, -1)$, $C(2, 9)$, and $D(-3, 6)$ and connect them in order. Find all the measurements of this shape (side lengths, perimeter, area, and angle measures) and based on that information, decide the most specific name for this shape. Justify your answer.

2. The spinner at right is only partially completed. Complete the spinner based on these clues.

   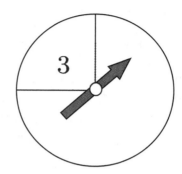

   a. There are three other single digit numbers on the spinner. All four numbers on the spinner are equally likely results for one spin. No digit is repeated.

   b. If the spinner is spun twice and the two outcomes are added, the largest possible sum is 16, while the smallest possible sum is 2. The most common sum is 9.

3. To go along with the snowflakes you are making for the winter dance decorating committee, you are going to make some "Star Polygons." A Star Polygon is formed by connecting equally spaced points on a circle in a specific order from a specified starting point.

   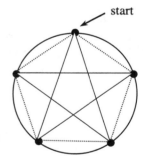

   For instance, the circle at right has five equally spaced points. If we connect them in order, the shape is a regular pentagon (dashed sides). But if we connect every other point, continuing until we reach the point that we started with, we get a star.

   a. What happens when 6 points are equally spaced around a circle? Under what conditions will you get a "normal" polygon, and when will you get a "star polygon"?

   b. Explore other options. Come up with a rule that explains when a normal polygon is formed when connecting points, and when a star polygon is formed. Consider various numbers of points.

   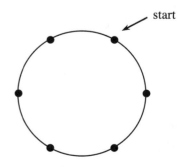

Answers

1. The side lengths are: $AB = CD = \sqrt{34} \approx 5.83$ units, $AD = CB = \sqrt{136} = 2\sqrt{34} \approx 11.66$ units. Perimeter $= 6\sqrt{34} \approx 34.99$ units. The slope of AB = the slope of CD = $\frac{3}{5}$, slope of AD = slope of CB = $-\frac{5}{3}$. Since the slopes are negative reciprocals, we know that the segments are perpendicular, so all four angles are 90°, so the figure is a rectangle. Area = 68 square units.

2. The spinner is divided into four equal pieces, with the numbers 3, 1, 6, and 8.

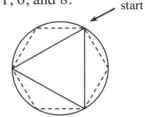

3. (a) Connecting consecutive points forms a hexagon. Connecting every other point forms an equilateral triangle. Connecting every third point forms several line segments (diameters), but no star.

   (b) Trying the same things with 7 points around a circle produces more interesting results. Connecting each point in order forms a heptagon (7-gon). Connecting every second point or every fifth point produces the first star polygon at right. Connecting every third point or every fourth point produces the second star polygon at right.

   Every second point
   or every fifth point

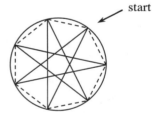

   Every third point
   or every fourth point

   To generalize, if the number of points around the circle is n, and we connect to the rth point, the polygon is a star polygon if n and r have no common factors. Note that whenever $r = 1$ or $r = n - 1$, the result is always a polygon.

Core Connections Geometry

Circles have special properties. The fact that they can roll smoothly is because the circle has a constant **diameter** (the distance across the circle that passes through the center). A vehicle with square wheels would cause it to bump up and down because, since the diagonals of a square are longer then its width, it does not have a constant diameter. But a circle is not the only shape with a constant diameter. Reuleaux curves, which resemble rounded polygons, also have a constant diameter. It may not appear to be the case, but Reuleaux curves roll smoothly without bumping up and down. See problem 7-3 in the textbook for a picture.

A circle does not include its interior. It is the set of points on a flat surface at a fixed distance (the radius) from a fixed point (the center). This also means that the center, diameters, and radii (plural of radius) are not part of the circle. Remember, a radius is half of a diameter, and connects the center of the circle to a point on the circle. A circle has infinitely many diameters and infinitely many radii.

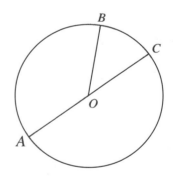

See the Math Notes box in Lesson 7.1.2.

Example 1

Using the circle at right, write an equation and solve for x. Note: Each part is a different problem.

a. $AO = 3x - 4, OB = 4x - 12$.

b. $OB = 2x - 5, AC = x - 7$

Using the information we have about circles, diameters, and radii, we can write an equation using the expressions in part (a), then solve for x. $\overline{AO}$ and $\overline{OB}$ are both radii of circle O, which means that they are equal in length.

$$AO = OB$$
$$3x - 4 = 4x - 12 \qquad \text{Subtract } 3x \text{ and add } 12 \text{ on both sides.}$$
$$8 = x$$

In part (b), $\overline{OB}$ is a radius, but $\overline{AC}$ is a diameter, so $\overline{AC}$ is twice as long as $\overline{OB}$.

$$2(OB) = AC$$
$$2(2x - 5) = x - 7$$
$$4x - 10 = x - 7$$
$$3x = 3$$
$$x = 1$$

Problems

Using the circle below, write an equation and solve for x. Note: Each part is a different problem.

1. $OP = 5x - 3, \ OR = 3x + 9$

2. $OQ = 2x + 12, \ OP = 3x - 1$

3. $OR = 12x - 8, \ OQ = 8x - 4$

4. $OP = 5x + 3, \ PR = 3x + 13$

5. $OQ = x - 6, \ PR = x + 7$

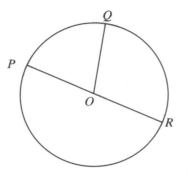

Answers

1. $x = 6$

2. $x = 13$

3. $x = 1$

4. $x = 1$

5. $x = 19$

Through the use of rigid transformations (rotations, reflections, and translations), students created new figures and discovered properties of these figures. Students also used transformations to discover the shortest path from one object to another (an optimization problem), and to define and study regular polygons. A **regular polygon** is a polygon in which all sides have equal length and all angles have equal measure.

See the Math Notes boxes in Lesson 7.1.4.

Example 1

On a recent scout camping trip, Zevel was walking back to camp when he noticed that the campfire had grown too large. He wants to fill his bucket at the river, then walk to the fire to douse the flames. To ensure the fire does not get out of control, Zevel wants to take the shortest path. What is the shortest path from where Zevel is standing to go to the river and then to the fire?

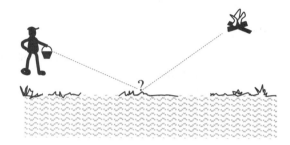

The shortest distance between two points on a flat surface is a straight line. How can we find the shortest distance if a third point is involved, such as Zevel's trip to the river? We use reflections to find the point at the river to which Zevel should walk. Reflecting across a line gives a new figure that is the same distance from the line as the original. Reflecting point F across the river line gives F' with $FX = F'X$. To find the shortest distance from Z to F' we connect them. Since $\angle FXR$ is a right angle, $\triangle FXR \cong \triangle F'XR$ by the SAS $\cong$ conjecture. This means that $FR = F'R$. Since the shortest path from Z to F' is the straight line drawn, then the shortest path from Zevel to the river and then to the fire is to walk from Z to R and then to F.

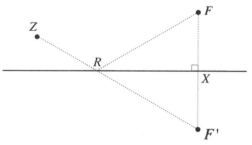

Example 2

If a hinged mirror is set at 10° and the core region (the region the hinged mirror encloses on the paper) is isosceles, how many sides would there be on the polygon that would be reflected in the mirror?

If the core region is isosceles, the reflected image will be a regular polygon. In a regular polygon, all the interior angles are equal in measure and, if the center is connected to each vertex of the polygon, these central angles are equal. If one central angle measures 10° and there are 360° around the center, there are 360° ÷ 10° = 36 sides on the polygon.

Problems

1. Venetia wants to install two lights in her garden. Each one will be connected to a control timer that will turn the lights on and off automatically. She can mount the timer anywhere on her house, but she wants to minimize the amount of wire she will use. If the wire must run from the light at point P to the timer, and then back out to the light at point Q, where should Venetia place the timer?

2. While playing miniature golf last weekend, Myrtle came to the fifth hole and saw that it was a par 1 hole. This meant that she should be able to putt the ball into the hole with one stroke. Explain to Myrtle how knowledge of "shortest distance" problems can help her make the putt.

3. If the center of a regular dodecagon (12 sides) is connected to each vertex of the figure, what is the measure of each angle at the center?

4. If a central angle of a regular polygon measures 18°, how many sides does the polygon have?

5. The center point of a regular pentagon is connected to each vertex forming five congruent isosceles triangles. Find the measure of each base angle in the isosceles triangles and use that result to find the measure of one interior angle of the pentagon.

Answers

1. Venetia should place the timer about 11.54 feet from the point X or 18.45 feet from the point Y on the diagram above.

2. If Myrtle can aim correctly and hit a straight shot, she can make a hole in one. She can imagine the hole reflected across the top boundary to find the direction to aim. If she hits the wall at the point X, the ball will travel to the hole.

3. 30°

4. 20 sides

5. Each base angle measures 54°. Two together makes one interior angle of the pentagon, so an interior angle measures 108°.

By tracing and reflecting triangles to form quadrilaterals, students discover properties about quadrilaterals. More importantly, they develop a method to prove that what they have observed is true. Students are already familiar with using flowcharts to organize information, so they will use flowcharts to present proofs. Since they developed their conjectures by reflecting triangles, their proofs will rely heavily on the triangle congruence conjectures developed in Chapter 6. Once students prove that their observations are true, they can use the information in later problems.

See the Math Notes boxes in Lessons 7.2.1, 7.2.3, 7.2.4, and 7.2.6.

Example 1

ABCD at right is a parallelogram. Use this fact and other properties and conjectures to prove that:

a.   the opposite sides are congruent.

b.   the opposite angles are congruent.

c.   the diagonals bisect each other.

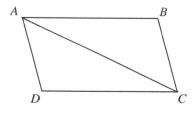

Because *ABCD* is a parallelogram, the opposite sides are parallel. Whenever we have parallel lines, we should be looking for some pairs of congruent angles. In this case, since *AB* ∥ *CD*, $\angle BAC \cong \angle DCA$ because alternate interior angles are congruent. Similarly, since *AD* ∥ *CB*, $\angle DAC \cong \angle BCA$. Also, $\overline{AC} \cong \overline{CA}$ by the Reflexive Property. Putting all three of these pieces of information together tells us that $\triangle BAC \cong \triangle DCA$ by the ASA ≅ conjecture. Now that we know that the triangles are congruent, all the other corresponding parts are also congruent. In particular, $\overline{AB} \cong \overline{CD}$ and $\overline{AD} \cong \overline{CB}$, which proves that the opposite sides are congruent. As a flowchart proof, this argument would be presented as shown below.

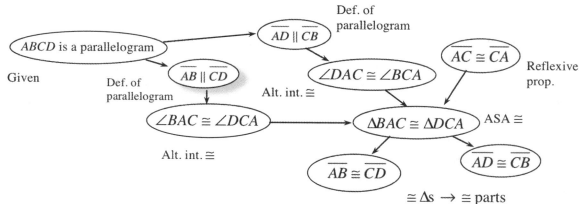

For part (b), we can continue the previous proof, again using congruent parts of congruent triangles, to justify that $\angle ADC \cong \angle CBA$. That gives one pair of opposite angles congruent. To get the other pair, we need to draw in the other diagonal. As before, the alternate interior angles are congruent, $\angle ADB \cong \angle CBD$ and $\angle ABD \cong \angle CDB$, because the opposite sides are parallel. Using the Reflexive Property, $\overline{BD} \cong \overline{BD}$. Therefore, $\triangle ABD \cong \triangle CDB$ by the ASA $\cong$ conjecture. Now that we know that the triangles are congruent, we can conclude that the corresponding parts are also congruent. Therefore, $\angle DAB \cong \angle BCD$. We have just proven that the opposite angles in the parallelogram are congruent.

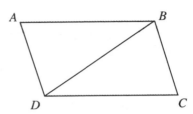

Lastly, we will prove that the diagonals bisect each other. To begin, we need a picture with both diagonals included. There are many triangles in the figure now, so our first task will be deciding which ones we should prove congruent to help us with the diagonals. To show that the diagonals bisect each other we will show that $\overline{AE} \cong \overline{CE}$ and $\overline{BE} \cong \overline{DE}$ since "bisect" means to cut into two equal parts.

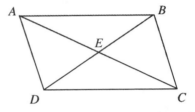

We have already proven facts about the parallelogram that we can use here. For instance, we know that the opposite sides are congruent, so $\overline{AD} \cong \overline{CB}$. We already know that the alternate interior angles are congruent, so $\angle ADE \cong \angle CBE$ and $\angle DAE \cong \angle BCE$. Once again we have congruent triangles: $\triangle ADE \cong \triangle CBE$ by ASA $\cong$. Since congruent triangles give us congruent corresponding parts, $\overline{AE} \cong \overline{CE}$ and $\overline{BE} \cong \overline{DE}$, which means the diagonals bisect each other.

Example 2

PQRS at right is a rhombus. Do the diagonals bisect each other? Justify your answer. Are the diagonals perpendicular? Justify your answer.

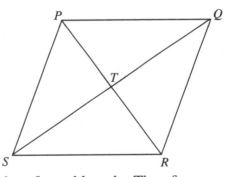

The definition of a rhombus is a quadrilateral with four sides of equal length. Therefore, $\overline{PQ} \cong \overline{QR} \cong \overline{RS} \cong \overline{SP}$. By the Reflexive Property, $\overline{PR} \cong \overline{RP}$. With sides congruent, we can use the SSS $\cong$ conjecture to write $\triangle SPR \cong \triangle QRP$. Since the triangles are congruent, all corresponding parts are also congruent. Therefore, $\angle SPR \cong \angle QRP$ and $\angle PRS \cong \angle RPQ$. The first pair of congruent angles means that $\overline{SP} \parallel \overline{QR}$. (If the alternate interior angles are congruent, the lines are parallel.) Similarly, the second pair of congruent angles means that $\overline{PQ} \parallel \overline{RS}$. With both pairs of opposite sides congruent, this rhombus is a parallelogram. Since it is a parallelogram, we can use what we have already proven about parallelograms, namely, that the diagonals bisect each other. Therefore, the answer is yes, the diagonals bisect each other.

Core Connections Geometry

To determine if the diagonals are perpendicular, use what we did to answer the first question. Then gather more information to prove that other triangles are congruent. In particular, since $\overline{PQ} \cong \overline{RQ}$, $\overline{QT} \cong \overline{QT}$, and $\overline{PT} \cong \overline{RT}$ (since the diagonal is bisected), $\Delta QPT \cong \Delta RQT$ by SSS $\cong$. Because the triangles are congruent, all corresponding parts are also congruent, so $\angle QTP \cong \angle QTR$. These two angles also form a straight angle. If two angles are congruent and their measures sum to 180°, each angle measures 90°. If the angles measure 90°, the lines must be perpendicular. Therefore, $\overline{QS} \perp \overline{PR}$.

Example 3

In the figure at right, if $\overline{AI}$ is the perpendicular bisector of $\overline{DV}$, is ΔDAV isosceles? Prove your conclusion using the two-column proof format.

Before starting a two-column proof, it is helpful to think about what we are trying to prove. If we want to prove that a triangle is isosceles, then we must show that $\overline{DA} \cong \overline{VA}$ because an isosceles triangle has two sides congruent. By showing that $\Delta AID \cong \Delta AIV$, we can then conclude that this pair of sides is congruent. Now that we have a plan, we can begin the two-column proof.

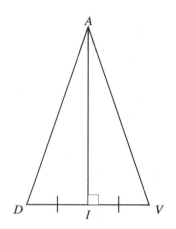

Statements	**Reason** (This statement is true because …)
$\overline{AI}$ is the perpendicular bisector of $\overline{DV}$	Given
$\overline{DI} \cong \overline{VI}$	Definition of bisector
$\angle DIA$ and $\angle VIA$ are right angles	Definition of perpendicular
$\angle DIA \cong \angle VIA$	All right angles are congruent
$\overline{AI} \cong \overline{AI}$	Reflexive Property of Equality
$\Delta DAI \cong \Delta VAI$	SAS $\cong$
$\overline{DA} \cong \overline{VA}$	$\cong \Delta s \rightarrow \cong$ parts
ΔDAV is isosceles	Definition of isosceles

Problems

Find the required information and justify your answers.

For problems 1-4 use the parallelogram at right.

1. Find the perimeter.

2. If $CT = 9$, find AT.

3. If $m\angle CDA = 60°$, find $m\angle CBA$ and $m\angle BAD$.

4. If $AT = 4x - 7$ and $CT = -x + 13$, solve for x.

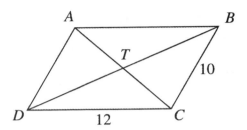

For problems 5-8 use the rhombus at right.

5. If $PS = \sqrt{6}$, what is the perimeter of $PQRS$?

6. If $PQ = 3x + 7$ and $QR = -x + 17$, solve for x.

7. If $m\angle PSM = 22°$, find $m\angle RSM$ and $m\angle SPQ$.

8. If $m\angle PMQ = 4x - 5$, solve for x.

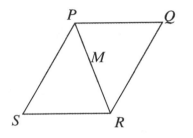

For problems 9-12 use the quadrilateral at right.

9. If $WX = YZ$ and $WZ = XY$, must $WXYZ$ be rectangle?

10. If $m\angle WZY = 90°$, must $WXYZ$ be a rectangle?

11. If the information in problems 9-10 are both true, must $WXYZ$ be a rectangle?

12. If $WY = 15$ and $WZ = 9$, what is YZ and XZ?

For problems 17-20 use the kite at right.

17. If $m\angle XWZ = 95°$, find $m\angle XYZ$.

18. If $m\angle WZY = 110°$ and $m\angle WXY = 40°$, find $m\angle ZWX$.

19. If $WZ = 5$ and $WT = 4$, find ZT.

20. If $WT = 4$, $TZ = 3$, and $TX = 10$, find the perimeter of $WXYZ$.

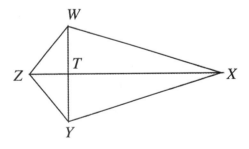

21. If $\overline{PQ} \cong \overline{RS}$ and $\overline{QR} \cong \overline{SP}$, is $PQRS$ a parallelogram? Prove your answer.

22. $WXYZ$ is a rhombus. Does $\overline{WY}$ bisect $\angle ZWX$? Prove your answer.

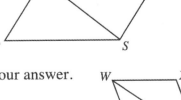

For problems 23-25, use the figure at right. Base your decision on the markings, not appearances.

23. Is $\triangle BCD \cong \triangle EDC$? Prove your answer.

24. Is $\overline{AB} \cong \overline{ED}$? Prove your answer.

25. Is $\overline{AB} \cong \overline{DC}$? Prove your answer.

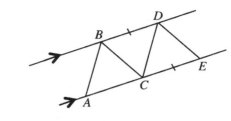

26. If *NIFH* is a parallelogram, is $\overline{ES} \cong \overline{ET}$? Prove your answer.

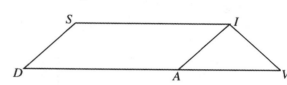

27. If *DSIA* is a parallelogram and $\overline{IA} \cong \overline{IV}$, is $\angle D \cong \angle V$? Prove your answer.

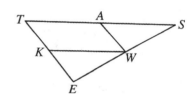

28. If *A*, *W*, and *K* are midpoints of $\overline{TS}$, $\overline{SE}$, and $\overline{ET}$ respectively, is *TAWK* a parallelogram? Prove your answer.

Answers

1. 44 units

2. 9 units

3. $60°, 120°$

4. 4

5. $4\sqrt{6}$

6. 2.5

7. $22°, 136°$

8. 23.75

9. no

10. no

11. yes

12. 12, 15

13. $60°$

14. 18.75

15. 8

16. 3

17. $95°$

18. $105°$

19. 3

20. $10 + 4\sqrt{29}$

21. Yes. $\overline{QS} \cong \overline{SQ}$ (reflexive). This fact, along with the given information means that $\triangle PQS \cong \triangle RSQ$ (SSS $\cong$). That tells us the corresponding parts are also congruent, so $\angle PQS \cong \angle RSQ$ and $\angle PSQ \cong \angle RQS$. These angles are alternate interior angles, so both pairs of opposite sides are parallel. Therefore, $PQRS$ is a parallelogram.

22. Yes. Since the figure is as a rhombus, all the sides are congruent. In particular, $\overline{WZ} \cong \overline{WX}$ and $\overline{ZY} \cong \overline{XY}$. Also, $\overline{WY} \cong \overline{WY}$ (reflexive), so $\triangle WZY \cong \triangle WXY$ (SSS $\cong$). Congruent triangles give us congruent parts so $\angle ZWY \cong \angle XWY$. Therefore, $\overline{WY}$ bisects $\angle ZWX$.

23. Yes. Since the lines are parallel, alternate interior angles are congruent so $\angle BDC \cong \angle ECD$. Also, $\overline{DC} \cong \overline{CD}$ (reflexive) so the triangles are congruent by SAS $\cong$.

24. Not necessarily, since we have no information about $\overline{AC}$.

25. Not necessarily.

26. Yes. Because $MIFH$ is a parallelogram, we know several things. First, $\angle TME \cong \angle SFE$ (alternate interior angles) and $\overline{ME} \cong \overline{EF}$ (diagonals of a parallelogram bisect each other). Also, $\angle TEM \cong \angle SEF$ because vertical angles are congruent. This gives us $\triangle MTE \cong \triangle FSE$ by ASA $\cong$. Therefore, the corresponding parts of the triangle are congruent, so $\overline{ES} \cong \overline{ET}$.

27. Since $DSIA$ is a parallelogram, $\overline{DS} \parallel \overline{AI}$ which gives us $\angle D \cong \angle IAV$ corresponding angles). Also, since $\overline{IA} \cong \overline{IV}$, $\triangle AIV$ is isosceles, so $\angle IAV \cong \angle V$. The two angle congruence statements allow us to conclude that $\angle D \cong \angle V$.

28. Yes. By the Triangle Midsegment Theorem (see the Math Notes box in Lesson 7.2.6), since A, W, and K are midpoints of $\overline{TS}$, $\overline{SE}$, and $\overline{ET}$ respectively, $\overline{AW} \parallel \overline{TE}$ and $\overline{KW} \parallel \overline{TS}$. Therefore $TAWK$ is a parallelogram.

Now that students are familiar with many of the properties of various triangles, quadrilaterals, and special quadrilaterals, they can apply their algebra skills and knowledge of the coordinate grid to study **coordinate geometry**. In this section, the shapes are plotted on a graph. Using familiar ideas, such as the Pythagorean Theorem and slope, students can prove whether or not quadrilaterals have special properties.

See the Math Notes boxes in Lessons 7.3.2 and 7.3.3.

Example 1

On a set of coordinate axes, plot the points $A(-3, -1)$, $B(1, -4)$, $C(5, -1)$, and $D(1, 2)$ and connect them in the order given. Is this quadrilateral a rhombus? Justify your answer.

To show that this quadrilateral is a rhombus, we must show that all four sides are the same length because that is the definition of a rhombus. When we want to find the length of a segment on the coordinate graph, we use the Pythagorean Theorem. To begin, we plot the points on a graph.

Although the shape appears to be a parallelogram, and possibly a rhombus, we cannot base our decision on appearances. To use the Pythagorean Theorem, we outline a **slope triangle**, creating a right triangle with $\overline{AB}$ as the hypotenuse. The lengths of the legs of this right triangle are 3 and 4 units. Using the Pythagorean Theorem,

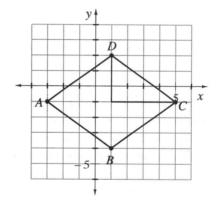

$$3^2 + 4^2 = (AB)^2$$
$$9 + 16 = (AB)^2$$
$$25 = (AB)^2$$
$$AB = 5$$

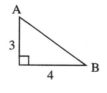

Similarly, we set up slope triangles for the other three sides of the quadrilateral and use the Pythagorean Theorem again. In each case, we find the lengths are all 5 units. Therefore, since all four sides have the same length, the figure is a rhombus.

Example 2

On a set of coordinate axes, plot the points $A(-4, 1)$, $B(1, 3)$, $C(8, -1)$, and $D(4, -3)$, and connect them in the order given. Is this quadrilateral a parallelogram? Prove your answer.

When we plot the points, the quadrilateral appears to be a parallelogram, but we cannot base our decision on appearances. To prove it is a parallelogram, we must show that the opposite sides are parallel. On the coordinate graph, we show that lines are parallel by showing that they have the same slope. We can use slope triangles to find the slope of each side.

Slope of $\overline{BC} = \frac{4}{-7} = -\frac{4}{7}$

Slope of $\overline{BA} = \frac{2}{5}$

Slope of $\overline{AD} = \frac{-4}{8} = -\frac{1}{2}$

Slope of $\overline{DC} = \frac{2}{4} = \frac{1}{2}$

Although the values for the slopes of the opposite sides are close, they are not equal. Therefore this quadrilateral is not a parallelogram.

Problems

1. If $ABCD$ is a rectangle, and $A(1, 2)$, $B(5, 2)$, and $C(5, 5)$, what is the coordinate of D?

2. If $P(2, 1)$ and $Q(6, 1)$ are the endpoints of the base of an isosceles right triangle, what is the x-coordinate of the third vertex?

3. The three points $S(-1, -1)$, $A(1, 4)$, and $M(2, -1)$ are vertices of a parallelogram. What are the coordinates of three possible points for the other vertex?

4. Graph the following lines on the same set of axes. These lines enclose a shape. What is the name of that shape? Justify your answer.

$$y = \tfrac{3}{5}x + 7 \qquad\qquad y = 0.6x$$
$$y = -\tfrac{10}{6}x - 1 \qquad\qquad y = -\tfrac{5}{3}x + 9$$

5. If $W(-4, -5)$, $X(1, 0)$, $Y(-1, 2)$, and $Z(-6, -3)$, what shape is $WXYZ$? Prove your answer.

6. If $\overline{DT}$ has endpoints $D(2, 2)$ and $T(6, 4)$, what is the equation of the perpendicular bisector of $\overline{DT}$?

Answers

1. $(1, 5)$

2. 4

3. $(4, 4), (0, -6),$ or $(-2, 4)$

4. Since the slopes of opposites side are equal, this is a parallelogram. Additionally, since the slopes of intersecting lines are negative reciprocals of each other, they are perpendicular. This means the angles are all right angles, so the figure is a rectangle.

5. The slopes are: $\overline{WX} = 1$, $\overline{XY} = -1$, $\overline{YZ} = 1$, and $\overline{ZW} = -1$. This shows that $WXYZ$ is a rectangle.

6. $y = -2x + 11$

After studying triangles and quadrilaterals, students now extend their study to all polygons. A polygon is a closed, two-dimensional figure made of three or more non-intersecting straight line segments connected end-to-end. Using the fact that the sum of the measures of the angles in a triangle is 180°, students learn a method to determine the sum of the measures of the interior angles of any polygon. Next they explore the sum of the measures of the exterior angles of a polygon. Finally they use the information about the angles of polygons along with their Triangle Toolkits to find the areas of regular polygons.

See the Math Notes boxes in Lessons 8.1.1, 8.1.5, and 8.3.1.

Example 1

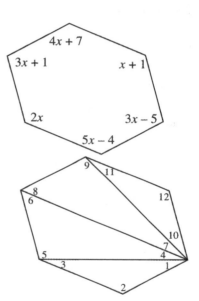

The figure at right is a hexagon. What is the sum of the measures of the interior angles of a hexagon? Explain how you know. Then write an equation and solve for x.

One way to find the sum of the interior angles of the hexagon is to divide the figure into triangles. There are several different ways to do this, but keep in mind that we are trying to add the interior angles at the vertices. One way to divide the hexagon into triangles is to draw in all of the diagonals from a single vertex, as shown at right. Doing this forms four triangles, each with angle measures summing to 180°.

$$\underbrace{m\angle 1 + m\angle 2 + m\angle 3}_{180°} + \underbrace{m\angle 4 + m\angle 5 + m\angle 6}_{180°} + \underbrace{m\angle 7 + m\angle 8 + m\angle 9}_{180°} + \underbrace{m\angle 10 + m\angle 11 + m\angle 12}_{180°}$$
$$= 4(180°) = 720°$$

(Note: Students may have noticed that the number of triangles is always two less than the number of sides. This example illustrates why the sum of the interior angles of a polygon may be calculated using the formula $(n-2)180°$, where n is the number of sides of the polygon.)

Now that we know what the sum of the angles is, we can write an equation, and solve for x.

$$(3x+1)+(4x+7)+(x+1)+(3x-5)+(5x-4)+(2x) = 720°$$
$$18x = 720°$$
$$x = 40°$$

Example 2

If the sum of the measures of the interior angles of a polygon is 2340°, how many sides does the polygon have?

Use the equation "sum of interior angles = $(n-2)180°$" to write an equation and solve for n. The solution is shown at right.

$$(n-2)\cdot180° = 2340°$$
$$180n - 360 = 2340$$
$$180n = 2700$$
$$n = 15$$

Since $n = 15$, the polygon has 15 sides. It is important to note that if the answer is not a whole number, an error was made or there is no polygon with its interior angles summing to the measure given. Since the answer is the number of sides, the answer can only be a whole number. Polygons cannot have "7.2" sides!

Example 3

What is the measure of an exterior angle of a regular decagon?

A decagon is a 10-sided polygon. Since this figure is a regular decagon, all the angles and all the sides are congruent. The sum of the measures of the exterior angles of any polygon, one at each vertex, is always 360°, no matter how many sides the polygon has. In this case the exterior angles are congruent since the decagon is regular. The decagon at right has ten exterior angles drawn, one at each vertex. Therefore, each angle measures $\frac{360°}{10} = 36°$.

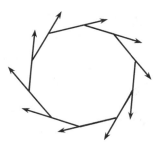

Example 4

A regular dodecagon (12 sided polygon) has a side length of 8 units. What is its area?

Solving this problem is going to require the use of several topics that have been studied. (Note: There is more than one way to solve this problem.) For this solution, we will imagine dividing the dodecagon into 12 congruent triangles, radiating from the center. If we find the area of one of them, then we can multiply it by 12 to get the area of the entire figure.

To focus on one triangle, copy and enlarge it. The triangle is isosceles, so drawing a segment from the vertex angle perpendicular to the base gives a height. This height also bisects the base (because this triangle is isosceles).

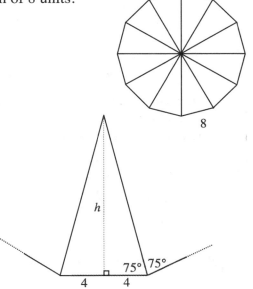

Since this is a dodecagon, we can find the sum of all the angles of the shape by using the formula:

$$(12 - 2)(180°) = 1800°$$

Since all the angles are congruent, each angle measures $1800° \div 12 = 150°$. The segments radiating from the center bisect each angle, so the base angle of the isosceles triangle is $75°$. Now we can use trigonometry to find h.

$$\tan 75° = \frac{h}{4}$$
$$h = 4 \tan 75°$$
$$h \approx 14.928$$

Therefore the area of one of these triangles is: $\quad A \approx \frac{1}{2}(8)(14.928) \approx 59.712$ square units

To find the area of the dodecagon, we multiply the area of one triangle by 12.

$$A \approx 12(59.712) \approx 716.544 \text{ square units}$$

Problems

Find the measures of the angles in each problem below.

1. Find the sum of the interior angles in a 7-gon.

2. Find the sum of the interior angles in an 8-gon.

3. Find the size of each of the interior angle of a regular 12-gon.

4. Find the size of each of the interior angle of a regular 15-gon.

5. Find the size of each of the exterior angle of a regular 17-gon.

6. Find the size of each of the exterior angle of a regular 21-gon.

Solve for x in each of the figures below.

7.

8. 5x 3x 2x 5x

9.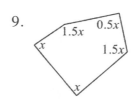

10. 5x 3x 5x 4x 2x 4x

Complete each of the following problems.

11. Each exterior angle of a regular n-gon measures $16\frac{4}{11}°$. How many sides does this n-gon have?

12. Each exterior angle of a regular n-gon measures $13\frac{1}{3}°$. How many sides does this n-gon have?

13. Each angle of a regular n-gon measures $156°$. How many sides does this n-gon have?

14. Each angle of a regular n-gon measures $165.6°$. How many sides does this n-gon have?

15. Find the area of a regular pentagon with side length 8 cm.

16. Find the area of a regular hexagon with side length 10 ft.

17. Find the area of a regular octagon with side length 12 m.

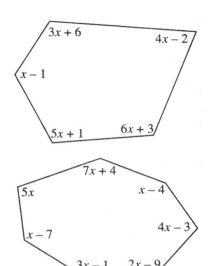

18. Find the area of a regular decagon with side length 14 in.

19. Using the pentagon at right, write an equation and solve for x.

20. Using the heptagon (7-gon) at right, write an equation and solve for x.

21. What is the sum of the measures of the interior angles of a 14-sided polygon?

22. What is the measure of each interior angle of a regular 16-sided polygon?

23. What is the sum of the measures of the exterior angles of a decagon (10-gon)?

24. Each exterior angle of a regular polygon measures 22.5°. How many sides does the polygon have?

25. Does a polygon exist whose sum of the interior angles is 3060°? If so, how many sides does it have? If not, explain why not.

26. Does a polygon exist whose sum of the interior angles is 1350°? If so, how many sides does it have? If not, explain why not.

27. Does a polygon exist whose sum of the interior angles is 4410°? If so, how many sides does it have? If not, explain why not.

28. In the figure at right, $ABCDE$ is a regular pentagon. Is $\overline{EB} \parallel \overline{DF}$? Justify your answer.

29. What is the area of a regular pentagon with a side length of 10 units?

30. What is the area of a regular 15-gon with a side length of 5 units?

Answers

1. $900°$

2. $1080°$

3. $150°$

4. $156°$

5. $21.1765°$

6. $17.1429°$

7. $x = 24°$

8. $x = 30°$

9. $x = 98.18°$

10. $x = 31.30°$

11. 22 sides

12. 27 sides

13. 15 sides

14. 25 sides

15. 110.1106 cm^2

16. 259.8076 ft^2

17. 695.2935 m^2

18. 1508.0649 in.^{2}

19. $19x + 7 = 540, x \approx 28.05$

20. $23x - 20 = 900, x = 40$

21. $2160°$

22. $157.5°$

23. $360°$

24. 16 sides

25. 19 sides

26. No. The result is not a whole number.

27. No. The result is not a whole number.

29. Yes. Since *ABCDE* is a regular pentagon, the measure of each interior angle is $108°$. Therefore, $m\angle DCB = 108°$. Since $\angle DCB$ and $\angle FCB$ are supplementary, $m\angle FCB = 72°$. The lines are parallel because the alternate interior angles are congruent.

30. ≈ 172.0 sq. units

31. ≈ 441.1 sq. units

Students return to similarity once again to explore what happens to the area of a figure if it is reduced or enlarged. In Chapter 3, students learned about the ratio of similarity, also called the "zoom factor." If two similar figures have a ratio of similarity of $\frac{a}{b}$, then the ratio of their perimeters is also $\frac{a}{b}$, while the ratio of their areas is $\frac{a^2}{b^2}$.

See the Math Notes boxes in Lessons 8.2.1 and 9.1.5.

Example 1

The figures P and Q at right are similar.

a.   What is the ratio of similarity?

b.   What is the perimeter of figure P?

c.   Use your previous two answers to find the perimeter of figure Q.

d.   If the area of figure P is 34 square units, what is the area of figure Q?

The ratio of similarity is the ratio of the lengths of two corresponding sides. In this case, since we only have the length of one side of figure Q, we will use the side of P that corresponds to that side. Therefore, the ratio of similarity is $\frac{3}{7}$.

To find the perimeter of figure P, add up all the side lengths: $3 + 6 + 4 + 5 + 3 = 21$. If the ratio of similarity of the two figures is $\frac{3}{7}$ then ratio of their perimeters is $\frac{3}{7}$ as well.

$$\frac{\text{perimeter } P}{\text{perimeter } Q} = \frac{3}{7}$$

$$\frac{21}{Q} = \frac{3}{7}$$

$$3Q = 147$$

$$\text{perimeter } Q = 49$$

If the ratio of similarity is $\frac{3}{7}$ then the ratio of the areas is $\left(\frac{3}{7}\right)^2 = \frac{9}{49}$.

$$\frac{\text{area } P}{\text{area } Q} = \left(\frac{3}{7}\right)^2$$

$$\frac{34}{Q} = \frac{9}{49}$$

$$9Q = 1666$$

$$\text{area } Q \approx 185.11 \text{ square units}$$

Example 2

Two rectangles are similar. If the area of the first rectangle is 49 square units, and the area of the second rectangle is 256 square units, what is the ratio of similarity between these two rectangles?

Since the rectangles are similar, if the ratio of similarity is $\frac{a}{b}$, then the ratio of their areas is $\frac{a^2}{b^2}$. We are given the areas so we know the ratio of their areas is $\frac{49}{256}$. Therefore we can write:

$$\frac{a^2}{b^2} = \frac{49}{256}$$

$$\frac{a}{b} = \sqrt{\frac{49}{256}} = \frac{\sqrt{49}}{\sqrt{256}} = \frac{7}{16}$$

The ratio of similarity between the two rectangles is $\frac{a}{b} = \frac{7}{16}$. This can be written as a decimal or as a fraction.

Problems

1. If figure A and figure B are similar with a ratio of similarity of $\frac{5}{4}$, and the perimeter of figure A is 18 units, what is the perimeter of figure B?

2. If figure A and figure B are similar with a ratio of similarity of $\frac{1}{8}$, and the area of figure A is 13 square units, what is the area of figure B?

3. If figure A and figure B are similar with a ratio of similarity of 6, that is, 6 to 1, and the perimeter of figure A is 54 units, what is the perimeter of figure B?

4. If figure A and figure B are similar and the ratio of their perimeters is $\frac{17}{6}$, what is their ratio of similarity?

5. If figure A and figure B are similar and the ratio of their areas is $\frac{32}{9}$, what is their ratio of similarity?

6. If figure A and figure B are similar and the ratio of their perimeters is $\frac{23}{11}$, does that mean the perimeter of figure A is 23 units and the perimeter of figure B is 11 units? Explain.

Answers

1. 14.4 units   2.   832 sq. units   3.   9 units   4. $\frac{17}{6}$ 5. $\frac{\sqrt{32}}{\sqrt{9}} \approx \frac{5.66}{3} \approx 1.89$

6. No, it just tells us the ratio. Figure A could have a perimeter of 46 units while figure B has a perimeter of 22 units.

Students have found the area and perimeter of several polygons. Next they consider what happens to the area as more and more sides are added to a polygon. By exploring the area of a polygon with many sides, they learn that the limit of a polygon is a circle. They extend what they know about the perimeter and area of polygons to circles, and find the relationships for the circumference (C) and area (A) of circles.

$$C = \pi d \text{ or } 2\pi r, \quad A = \pi r^2$$

"C" is the circumference of the circle (a circle's perimeter), "d" is the diameter, and "r" is the radius. "π," which is in both formulas, is by definition the ratio $\frac{\text{circumference}}{\text{diameter}}$, and it is always a constant for any size circle.

Using these formulas, along with ratios, students are able to find the perimeter and area of shapes containing parts of circles.

See the Math Notes boxes in Lessons 7.1.2, 8.3.2, and 8.3.3.

Example 1

The circle at right has a radius of 8 cm. What are the circumference and the area of the circle?

Using the formulas,

$$C = 2\pi r \qquad\qquad A = \pi r^2$$
$$\quad = 2\pi(8) \qquad\qquad = \pi(8)^2$$
$$\quad = 16\pi \qquad\qquad\quad = 64\pi$$
$$\quad \approx 50.27 \text{ cm} \qquad\quad \approx 201.06 \text{ sq. cm}$$

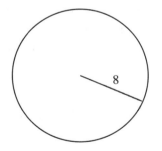

Example 2

Hermione has a small space on her corner lot that she would like to turn into a patio. To do this, she needs to do two things. First, she must know the length of the curved part, where she will put some decorative edging. Second, with the edging in place, she will need to purchase concrete to cover the patio. The concrete is sold in bags. Each bag will fill 2.5 square feet to the required depth of four inches. How much edging and concrete should Hermione buy?

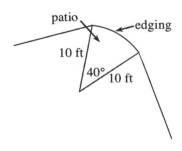

The edging is a portion of the circumference of a circle with the center at point O and a radius of 10 feet. We can determine the exact fraction of the circle by looking at the measure of the central angle. Since the angle measures 40°, and there are 360° in the whole circle, this portion is $\frac{40°}{360°} = \frac{1}{9}$ of the circle. If we find the circumference and area of the whole circle, then we can take $\frac{1}{9}$ of each of those measurements to find the portion needed.

$$C = \tfrac{1}{9}(2\pi r) \qquad\qquad A = \tfrac{1}{9}\pi r^2$$
$$= \tfrac{1}{9}(2 \cdot \pi \cdot 10) \qquad\qquad = \tfrac{1}{9} \cdot \pi \cdot (10)^2$$
$$= \tfrac{20\pi}{9} \approx 6.98 \text{ feet} \qquad\qquad = \tfrac{100\pi}{9} \approx 34.91 \text{ square feet}$$

Hermione should buy 7 feet of edging, and she should buy 14 bags of concrete ($34.91 \div 2.5 \approx 13.96$ bags). Concrete is sold in full bags only.

Example 3

Rubeus' dog Fluffy is tethered to the side of his house at point X. If Fluffy's rope is 18 feet long, how much area does Fluffy have to run in?

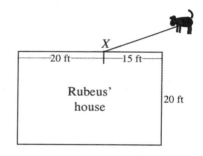

Because Fluffy is tethered to a point by a rope, he can only go where the rope can reach. Assuming that there are no obstacles, this area would be circular. Since Fluffy is blocked by the house, the area will only be a portion of a circle.

From point X, Fluffy can reach 18 feet to the left and right of point X. This initial piece is a semicircle. But, to the right of point X, the rope will bend around the corner of the house, adding a little more area for Fluffy. This smaller piece is a quarter of a circle with a radius of 3 feet.

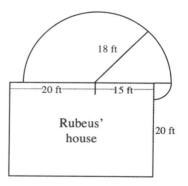

Semicircle:
$$A = \tfrac{1}{2}\pi r^2$$
$$= \tfrac{18^2\pi}{2}$$
$$= \tfrac{324\pi}{2}$$
$$= 162\pi \approx 508.94$$

Quarter circle:
$$A = \tfrac{1}{4}\pi r^2$$
$$= \tfrac{3^2\pi}{4}$$
$$= \tfrac{9\pi}{4}$$
$$\approx 7.07$$

Fluffy has a total of $508.94 + 7.07 \approx 516$ square feet in which to run.

Problems

Find the area of the shaded sector in each circle below. Points A, B, and C are the centers.

1.

2.

3.

Calculate the area of the following shaded sectors. Point O is the center of each circle.

4.

5.

6.

7.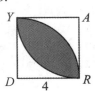

8. The shaded region in the figure is called a segment of the circle. It can be found by subtracting the area of $\triangle MIL$ from the sector MIL. Find the area of the segment of the circle.

9.

10.

11. *YARD* is a square; A and D are the centers of the arcs.

12. Find the area of a circular garden if the diameter of the garden is 30 feet.

13. Find the area of a circle inscribed in a square whose diagonal is 8 feet long.

14. The area of a 60° sector of a circle is 10π m². Find the radius of the circle.

15. The area of a sector of a circle with a radius of 5 mm is 10π mm². Find the measure of its central angle.

Find the area of each shaded region.

16.

10 m
10 m
60° 60°

17.

14 ft
14 ft

18.

4 in.

19.

r = 8

20.

60°
$r_{small} = 5$
$r_{large} = 8$

21.

12
12 (left)

22. Find the length of the radius. The shaded area is 12π cm².

120° r

Find the area of the shaded sector in each circle below. In each case, point O is the center.

23.

O
45°
4

24.

7
120°
O

25.

O
11

26.
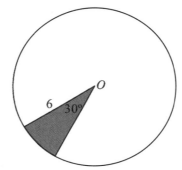
O
6
30°

27. Find the arc length of the shaded sector in problem 1.

28. Find the arc length of the shaded sector in problem 2.

29. Find the arc length of the shaded sector in problem 3.

30. Find the arc length of the shaded sector in problem 4.

31. Kennedy and Tess are constructing a racetrack for their horses. The track encloses a field that is rectangular, with two semicircles at each end. A fence must surround this field. How much fencing will Kennedy and Tess need?

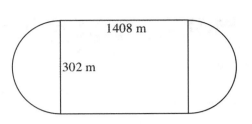

32. Rubeus has moved his dog Fluffy to a corner of his barn because he wants him to have more room to run. If Fluffy is tethered at point X on the barn with a 20 foot rope, how much area does Fluffy have to explore?

Answers

1. 2π units^2

2. $\frac{49}{3}\pi$ units^2

3. $\frac{363\pi}{4}$ units^2

4. $\frac{\pi}{2}$ units^2

5. 12π units^2

6. $\frac{931\pi}{36}$ units^2

7. 5π units^2

8. $\pi - 2$ units^2

9. $\frac{100}{3}\pi - 25\sqrt{3}$ units^2

10. $10\pi - 20$ units^2

11. $8\pi - 16$ units^2

12. 225π ft^2

13. 8π ft^2

14. $2\sqrt{15}$ m

15. $144°$

16. $100 - \frac{25}{3}\pi$ m^2

17. $196 - 49\pi$ ft^2

18. 10π in.^{2}

19. $48\pi + 32$ units^2

20. $\frac{65}{2}\pi$ units^2

21. ≈ 61.8 units^2

22. 6 cm

23. $2\pi \approx 6.28$ sq. units

24. $\frac{49}{3}\pi \approx 51.31$ sq. units

25. $\frac{363\pi}{4} \approx 285.10$ sq. units

26. $3\pi \approx 9.42$ sq. units

27. $\pi + 8 \approx 11.14$ units

28. $\frac{14\pi}{3} + 14 \approx 28.66$ units

29. $\frac{33\pi}{2} + 22 \approx 73.84$ units

30. $\pi + 12 \approx 15.14$ units

31. $2816 + 302\pi \approx 3764.76$ meters of fencing

32. $200\pi + 100\pi + \frac{25\pi}{4} \approx 962.11$ square feet

In this chapter, students examine three-dimensional shapes, known as solids. Students will work on visualizing these solids by building and then drawing them. Visualization is a useful, often overlooked skill in mathematics. By drawing solids students gain a better understanding of volume and surface area.

See the Math Notes boxes in Lessons 9.1.2, 9.1.3, and 9.1.5.

Example 1

The solid at right is built from individual cubes (blocks) stacked upon each other on a flat surface. (This means that no cubes are "floating.") Create a mat plan representing this solid. What is the volume of this solid?

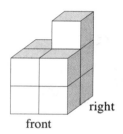

front   right

This solid consists of stacked blocks. We are looking at the front, right side, and top of this solid. A mat plan shows a different perspective of a solid. It shows the footprint of the solid as well as how many blocks are in each stack. A mat plan is useful because, in the solid above, we cannot see the possible "hidden" blocks. A mat plan tells us exactly how many blocks are in the solid.

In this case, since we are creating the mat plan from the stacked blocks, there is more than one possible answer. If there are no hidden blocks, then the mat plan is the first diagram at right. If there is a hidden block, then the mat plan is the second one at right. It is helpful to visualize solids by building them with cubes. Build solids on a 3 × 5 card so that you can rotate the card to see the solid from all of its sides. Do this to make sure that one block is all that can be hidden in this drawing.

TWO POSSIBLE
MAT PLANS

2	3
2	2

Front
no hidden
blocks

	1
2	3
2	2

Front
hidden
block

The volume of this solid is the number of cubes it would take to build it. In this case, the volume is either 9 cubic units or 10 cubic units.

Example 2

At right is a mat plan of a solid. Build the solid. What is the volume of this solid? Draw the front, right, and top views, as well as the three-dimensional view of this solid.

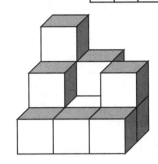

We find the volume by counting the number of blocks it would take to build this solid or by adding the numbers in the mat plan. The volume of this solid is 12 cubic units. To draw the different views of this solid, it is extremely helpful to build it out of cubes on a 3 × 5 card. Label the card with front, right, left, and back so that you can remember which side is which when rotating it. Remember that the standard three-dimensional view shows the top, right, and front views.

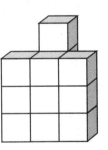

The individual views of each side are flat views. It is helpful to look at the solid at your eye level, so that only one side is visible at a time.

Front   Right   Top

Example 3

If the figure at right is made with the fewest amount of cubes possible, what is its surface area?

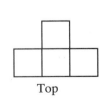

The surface area is the sum of the areas of all the surfaces (or faces or sides) on the solid. If we build the solid on a card, then we can rotate the card and count the number of squares on each face, except the bottom. Note that because we never have floating cubes in our solids, the bottom has the same surface area as the top. If we draw every face of the solid, we can count the number of squares to find the surface area. Alternately, rather than drawing every face, we can draw only three views — the front, right, and top — and double those areas, because the back, left, and bottom are always their reflections with equivalent respective areas. Either way, we will arrive at the same answer.

From the front and back the solid looks the same and shows 10 squares.

The right and left views are reflections of each other and each shows seven squares.

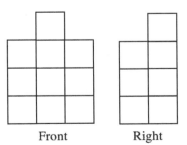

The top and bottom views are also reflections of each other. They show four squares each.

Therefore, the surface area is 10 + 10 + 7 + 7 + 4 + 4 = 42 square units.

Example 4

The dimensions of the prism at right are shown. What are the volume and surface area of this prism?

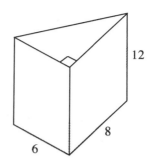

A prism is a special type of polyhedron that has two congruent and parallel bases. In this problem, the bases are right triangles. The volume of a prism is found by multiplying the area of the base by the height of the prism. To understand this process, think of a prism as a stack of cubes. The base area tells you how many cubes are in one layer of the stack. The height tells you how many layers of cubes are in the figure.

In this example, the base is a right triangle, so the area is $\frac{1}{2}bh$. Looking at the top of the prism might make it easier to find the area of the base represented by A_b.
$A_b = \frac{1}{2}bh = \frac{1}{2}(6)(8) = 24$ square units, so there are 24 cubes in one layer.

To find the volume, we multiply this amount by the height, 12.

$$V = A_b h = (24)(12) = 288 \text{ cubic units}$$

To find the surface area of this prism, we will find the area of each of its faces, including the bases, and add the areas. One way to illustrate the sub-problems is to make sketches of the surfaces.

$$\text{Surface Area} = 2\left(\,\boxed{\triangle}\,8 \atop 6\right) + \boxed{}\,12 \atop 6 \; + \; \boxed{}\,12 \atop 8 \; + \; \boxed{}\,12 \atop ?$$

All of the surfaces are familiar shapes, namely, triangles and rectangles. We need to calculate the length of the rectangle on the back face (the last rectangle in the pictorial equation above). Fortunately, that length is also the hypotenuse of the right triangle of the base, so we can use the Pythagorean Theorem to find that length.

$$6^2 + 8^2 = ?^2$$
$$36 + 64 = ?^2$$
$$?^2 = 100$$
$$? = \sqrt{100} = 10$$

Therefore the surface area is:

$$\text{S.A.} = 2\left(\tfrac{1}{2} \cdot 6 \cdot 8\right) + (6 \cdot 12) + (8 \cdot 12) + (10 \cdot 12)$$
$$= 48 + 72 + 96 + 120$$
$$= 336 \text{ square units}$$

Example 5

The Styrofoam pieces used in packing boxes, known as "shipping peanuts," are sold in three box sizes: small, medium, and large. The small box has a volume of 1200 cubic inches. The dimensions on the "medium" box are twice the dimensions of the small box, and the "large" box has triple the dimensions of the small one. All three boxes are similar prisms. What are volumes of the medium and large boxes?

Since the boxes are similar, we can use the ratio of similarity to determine the volume of the medium and large boxes without knowing their actual dimensions. When figures are similar with ratio of similarity $\frac{a}{b}$, the ratio of the areas is $(\frac{a}{b})^2$ and the ratio of the volumes is $(\frac{a}{b})^3$. Since the medium box has dimensions twice the small box and the large box has dimensions three times the small box, we can write:

$$\frac{\text{medium box}}{\text{small box}} = \frac{2}{1} \qquad\qquad \frac{\text{large box}}{\text{small box}} = \frac{3}{1}$$

$$\frac{\text{volume of medium box}}{\text{volume of small box}} = \left(\frac{2}{1}\right)^3 \qquad\qquad \frac{\text{volume of large box}}{\text{volume of small box}} = \left(\frac{3}{1}\right)^3$$

$$\frac{V_m}{1200} = \frac{8}{1} \qquad\qquad \frac{V_l}{1200} = \frac{27}{1}$$

Solving, $V_m = 8 \cdot 1200$ or $V_m = 9600$ cubic units and $V_l = 27 \cdot 1200$ or $V_l = 32{,}400$ cubic units.

Problems

For each solid, calculate the volume and surface area, then draw a mat plan. Assume there are no hidden or floating cubes.

1.

2.

3.

For each mat plan, draw the solid, then calculate the volume and surface area.

4.

	2	2
5	4	1
4	1	1

5.

2	2	1
2		1
1	1	1

6.

3	3	2
	2	2
1	1	1

Calculate the volume and surface area of each prism.

7.

The base is a rectangle.

8.

9.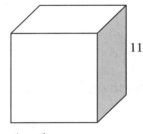

A cube.

10. At Cakes R Us, it is possible to buy round cakes in different sizes. The smallest cake has a diameter of 8 inches and a height of 4 inches, and requires 3 cups of batter. Another similar round cake has a diameter of 13 inches. How much batter would this cake require?

11. Prism A and prism B are similar with a ratio of similarity of 2:3. If the volume of prism A is 36 cubic units, what is the volume of prism B?

12. Two rectangular prisms are similar. The smaller, A, has a height of 4 units while the larger, B, has a height of 6 units.

    a. What is the scale factor from prism A to prism B?

    b. What is the ratio of the lengths of the edges labeled x and y?

    c. What is the ratio of their surface areas? What is the ratio of their volumes?

    d. A third prism C is similar to prisms A and B. Prism C's height is 10 units. If the volume of prism A is 24 cubic units, what is the volume of prism C?

13. Two rectangular prisms are similar. The smaller, A, has a height of 4 units while the larger, B, has a height of 6 units.

    a. What is the scale factor from prism B to prism A?

    b. What would be the ratio of the lengths of the edges labeled x and y?

    c. What is the ratio of their surface areas? What is the ratio of their volumes?

    d. A third prism, C is similar to prisms A and B. Prism C's height is 10 units. If the volume of prism A is 20 cubic units, what is the volume of prism C?

14. If rectangle A and rectangle B have a ratio of similarity of 5:4, what is the area of rectangle B if the area of rectangle A is 24 square units?

15. If rectangle *A* and rectangle *B* have a ratio of similarity of 2:3, what is the area of rectangle *B* if the area of rectangle *A* is 46 square units?

16. If rectangle *A* and rectangle *B* have a ratio of similarity of 3:4, what is the area of rectangle *B* if the area of rectangle *A* is 82 square units?

17. If rectangle *A* and rectangle *B* have a ratio of similarity of 1:5, what is the area of rectangle *B* if the area of rectangle *A* is 24 square units?

18. Rectangle *A* is similar to rectangle *B*. The area of rectangle *A* is 81 square units while the area of rectangle *B* is 49 square units. What is the ratio of similarity between the two rectangles?

19. Rectangle *A* is similar to rectangle *B*. The area of rectangle *B* is 18 square units while the area of rectangle *A* is 12.5 square units. What is the ratio of similarity between the two rectangles?

20. Rectangle *A* is similar to rectangle *B*. The area of rectangle *A* is 16 square units while the area of rectangle *B* is 100 square units. If the perimeter of rectangle *A* is 12 units, what is the perimeter of rectangle *B*?

21. If prism *A* and prism *B* have a ratio of similarity of 2:3, what is the volume of prism *B* if the volume of prism *A* is 36 cubic units?

22. If prism *A* and prism *B* have a ratio of similarity of 1:4, what is the volume of prism *B* if the volume of prism *A* is 83 cubic units?

23. If prism *A* and prism *B* have a ratio of similarity of 6:11, what is the volume of prism *B* if the volume of prism *A* is 96 cubic units?

24. Prism *A* and prism *B* are similar. The volume of prism *A* is 72 cubic units while the volume of prism *B* is 1125 cubic units. What is the ratio of similarity between these two prisms?

25. Prism *A* and prism *B* are similar. The volume of prism *A* is 27 cubic units while the volume of prism *B* is approximately 512 cubic units. If the surface area of prism *B* is 128 square units, what is the surface area of prism *A*?

26. The corresponding diagonals of two similar trapezoids are in the ratio of 1:7. What is the ratio of their areas?

27. The ratio of the perimeters of two similar parallelograms is 3:7. What is the ratio of their areas?

28. The ratio of the areas of two similar trapezoids is 1:9. What is the ratio of their altitudes?

29. The areas of two circles are in the ratio of 25:16. What is the ratio of their radii?

30. The ratio of the volumes of two similar circular cylinders is 27:64. What is the ratio of the diameters of their similar bases?

31. The surface areas of two cubes are in the ratio of 49:81. What is the ratio of their volumes?

32. The ratio of the weights of two spherical steel balls is 8:27. What is the ratio of the diameters of the two steel balls?

Answers

1.   V = 7 cu. units

     SA = 28 sq. units

2.   V = 10 cu. units

     SA = 36 sq. units

3.   V = 12 cu. units

     SA = 38 sq. units

4. V = 20 cu. units
   SA = 60 sq. units

5. V = 11 cu. units
   SA = 36 sq. units

6. V = 15 cu. units
   SA = 46 sq. units

7. V = 630 cu. units
   SA = 482 sq. units

8. V = 45 cu. units
   SA = 91.8 sq. units

9. V = 1331 cu. units
   SA = 726 sq. units

10. ≈ 12.87 cups

11. 121.5 cu. units

12. a. $\frac{4}{6} = \frac{2}{3}$ b. $\frac{x}{y} = \frac{4}{6} = \frac{2}{3}$ c. $\frac{16}{36} = \frac{4}{9}$, $\frac{64}{216} = \frac{8}{27}$ d. 375 cu. units

13. a. $\frac{6}{2} = \frac{3}{1}$ b. $\frac{x}{y} = \frac{2}{6} = \frac{1}{3}$ c. $\frac{4}{36} = \frac{1}{9}$, $\frac{8}{216} = \frac{1}{27}$ d. 2500 cu. units

14. 15.36 units^2 15. 103.5 units^2 16. ≈ 145.8 units^2 17. 600 units^2

18. $\frac{9}{7}$ 19. $\frac{6}{5}$ 20. 30 units   21. 121.5

22. 5312   23. ≈ 591.6   24. $\frac{2}{5}$ 25. ≈ 18 units^2

26. $\frac{1}{49}$ 27. $\frac{9}{49}$ 28. $\frac{1}{3}$ 29. $\frac{5}{4}$

30. $\frac{3}{4}$ 31. $\frac{343}{729}$ 32. $\frac{2}{3}$

The remainder of the chapter introduces constructions. Historically, before there were uniform measuring devices, straightedges and compasses were the only means to draw shapes. A straightedge is not a ruler in that it has no measurement markings on it. Despite the fact that students do not have access to rulers or protractors in this part of the chapter, they are still able to draw shapes, create some specific angle measurements, bisect angles and segments, and copy congruent figures.

See the Math Notes boxes in Lessons 9.2.3 and 9.2.4.

Example 1

Using only a straightedge and compass, construct the perpendicular bisector of $\overline{AB}$ at right. Then bisect one of the right angles.

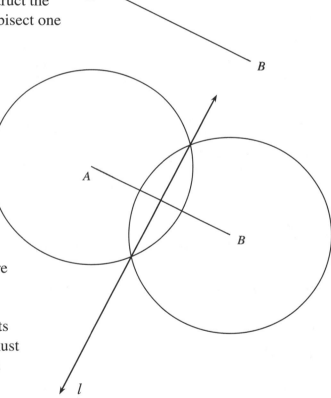

The perpendicular bisector of $\overline{AB}$ is a line that is perpendicular to $\overline{AB}$ and also goes through the midpoint of $\overline{AB}$. Although we could find this line by folding point A onto point B, we want a way to find it with just the straightedge and compass. Also, with no markings on the straightedge, we cannot measure to find the midpoint.

Because of the nature of a compass, circles are the basis for constructions. For this construction, we draw two congruent circles, one with its center at point A, the other with its center at point B. The radii of these circles must be large enough so that the circles intersect at two points. Drawing a line through the two intersection points of intersection gives l, the perpendicular bisector of $\overline{AB}$.

To bisect a right angle, we begin by drawing a circle with a center at point M. There are no restrictions on the length of the radius, but we need to see the points of intersection, P and Q. Also, we are only concerned with the arc of the circle that is within the interior of the angle we are bisecting, $\overset{\frown}{PQ}$. Next we use points P and Q as the centers of two congruent circles that intersect in the interior of ∠PMQ. This gives us point X which, when connected to point M, bisects the right angle.

Note: With this construction, we have created two 45° angles. From this we also get a 135° angle, ∠XMA. Another bisection (of ∠XMQ) would give us a 22.5° angle.

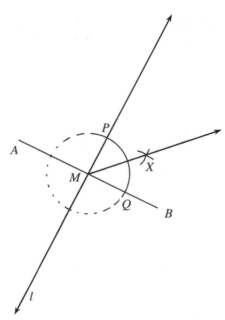

Example 2

Construct △MUD so that △MUD is congruent to △ABC by SAS ≅.

To construct a congruent triangle, we will need to use two constructions: copying a segment and copying an angle. In this example we want to construct the triangle with the SAS ≅, so we will copy a side, then an angle, and then the adjacent side. It does not matter which side we start with as long as we do the remainder of the parts in a SAS order. Here we will start by copying $\overline{BC}$ with a compass. First draw a ray like the one at right. Next, put the compass point on point B and open the compass so that it reaches to point C. Keeping that measurement, mark off a congruent segment on the ray ($\overline{UD}$). Next copy ∠BCA so that its vertex C is at point D on the ray and one of its sides is $\overline{UD}$. Then copy $\overline{CA}$ to create $\overline{DM}$. Finally, connect point U to point M and △MUD ≅ △ABC.

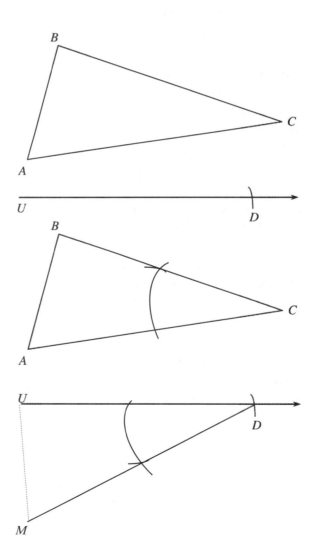

Problems

1. Construct a triangle congruent to △*XYZ* using SSS ≅.

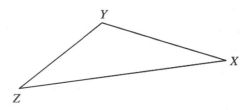

2. Construct a rhombus with sides congruent to $\overline{AB}$.

3. Construct a regular hexagon with sides congruent to $\overline{PQ}$.

4. Use constructions to find the centroid of △*WKD*.

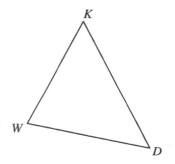

5. Construct the perpendicular bisectors of each side of △*TES*. Do they all meet in one point?

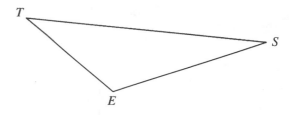

Answers

1. Draw a ray and copy one side of $\triangle XYZ$ on it—for example, $\overline{XZ}$. Copy a second side ($\overline{XY}$), put one endpoint at X, and swing an arc above $\overline{XZ}$. Finally, copy the third side, place the compass point at Z, and swing an arc above $\overline{XZ}$ so that it intersects the arc from X. Connect points X and Z to the point of intersection of the arcs and label it Y.

2. Copy $\overline{AB}$ on a ray. Draw another ray from A above the ray and mark a point C on it at the length of $\overline{AB}$. Swing arcs of length $\overline{AB}$ from B and C and label their intersection D.

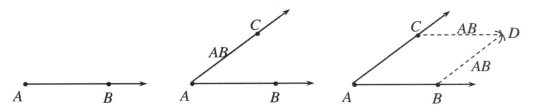

3. Construct a circle of radius $\overline{PQ}$. Mark a point on the circle, then make consecutive arcs around the circle using length PQ. Connect the six points to form the hexagon. Alternately, construct an equilateral triangle using $\overline{PQ}$, then make five copies of the triangle to complete the hexagon.

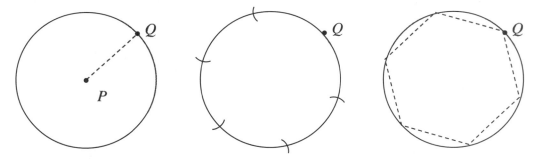

4. Bisect each side of $\triangle WKD$, then draw a segment from each vertex to the midpoint of the opposite side. The point where the medians intersect is the centroid.

5. Yes.

Students revisit circles in the first part of Chapter 10 to develop "circle tools," which will help them find lengths and angle measures within circles. In addition to working with the lengths of the radius and diameter of a circle, they will gain information about angles, arcs, and chords. As with the development of many topics we have studied, triangles will again be utilized.

See the Math Notes boxes in Lessons 10.1.1, 10.1.2, 10.1.3, 10.1.4, and 10.1.5.

Example 1

In the circle at right are two chords, $\overline{AB}$ and $\overline{CD}$. Find the center of the circle and label it P.

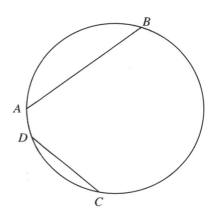

The chords of a circle (segments with endpoints on the circle) are useful segments. In particular, the diameter is a special chord that passes through the center. The perpendicular bisectors of the chords pass through the center of the circle as well. Therefore to find the center, we will find the perpendicular bisectors of each segment. They will meet at the center.

There are several ways to find the perpendicular bisectors of the segments. A quick way is to fold the paper so that the endpoints of the chords come together. The crease will be perpendicular to the chord and bisect it. Another method is to use the construction we learned last chapter. In either case, point P is the center of the circle.

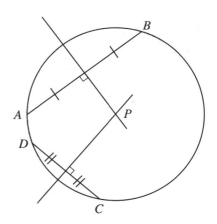

Example 2

In ⊙O at right, use the given information to find the values of x, y, and z.

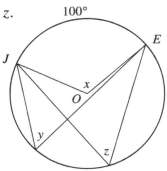

Pieces of a circle are called arcs, and every arc breaks the circle into two pieces. The large piece is called a major arc, and the smaller piece is called a minor arc. Arcs have lengths, and we found lengths of arcs by finding a fraction of the circumference. But arcs also have measures based on the measure of the corresponding central angle. In the picture at right, ∠JOE is a central angle since its vertex is at the center, O. An arc's measure is the same as its central angle. Since $\overset{\frown}{JE} = 100°$, $x = 100°$.

An angle with its vertex on the circle is called an inscribed angle. Both of the angles y and z are inscribed angles. Inscribed angles measure half of their intercepted arc (in this case, $\overset{\frown}{JE}$). Therefore, $y = z = \frac{1}{2}(100°) = 50°$.

Example 3

In the figure at right, O is the center of the circle. $\overrightarrow{TX}$ and $\overrightarrow{TB}$ are tangent to ⊙O , and $m\angle BOX = 120°$. Find the $m\angle BTX$.

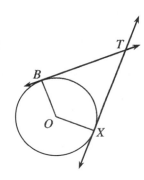

If a line is tangent to a circle, that line intersects the circle in only one point. Also, a radius drawn to the point of tangency is perpendicular to the tangent line. Therefore we know that $\overline{OB} \perp \overline{BT}$ and $\overline{OX} \perp \overline{XT}$. At this point there are different ways to solve this problem. One way is to add a segment to the picture. Adding $\overline{OT}$ will create two triangles, and we know a lot of information about triangles. In fact, these two right triangles are congruent by HL ≅ ($\overline{OB} \cong \overline{OX}$ because they are both radii, and $\overline{OT} \cong \overline{OT}$). Since the corresponding parts of congruent triangles are also congruent, and $m\angle BOX = 120°$, we know that $m\angle BOT = m\angle XOT = 60°$. Using the sum of the angles of a triangle is 180°, we find $m\angle BTO = m\angle XTO = 30°$. Therefore, $m\angle BTX = 60°$.

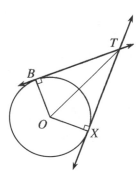

An alternate solution is to note that the two right angles at points B and X, added to ∠BOX, make 300°. Since we know that the angles in a quadrilateral sum to 360°, $m\angle BTX = 360° - 300° = 60°$.

Example 4

In the circle at right, $DV = 9$ units, $SV = 12$ units, and $AV = 4$ units. Find the length of IV.

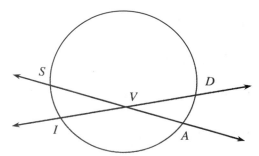

Although we have been concentrating on angles and their measures, there are some facts about lengths of chords of circles that are useful (and should be part of your "circle tools"). In the figure above, if we drew $\overline{SI}$ and $\overline{DA}$ we would form two similar triangles. (See the Math Notes box in Lesson 10.1.4.) The sides of similar triangles are proportional, so we can write the proportion at right, which leads to the simplified equation with the two products.

$$\frac{SV}{DV} = \frac{IV}{AV}$$

$$SV \cdot AV = DV \cdot IV$$

Substitute the lengths that we know, then solve the equation.

$$\frac{SV}{DV} = \frac{IV}{AV}$$
$$\frac{12}{9} = \frac{IV}{4}$$
$$9\,IV = 48$$
$$IV \approx 5.33 \text{ units}$$

Problems

Find each measure in $\odot P$ if $m\angle WPX = 28°$, $m\angle ZPY = 38°$, and $\overline{WZ}$ and $\overline{XV}$ are diameters.

1. $\overparen{YZ}$
2. $\overparen{WX}$
3. $\angle VPZ$
4. $\overparen{VWX}$

5. $\angle XPY$
6. $\overparen{XY}$
7. $\overparen{XWY}$
8. $\overparen{WZX}$

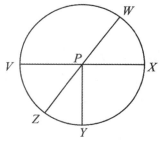

In each of the following figures, O is the center of the circle. Calculate the value of x and justify your answer.

9.

10.

11.

12.

13.

14.

15.

16.

17.

18.

19.

20.

In $\odot O$, $m\overset{\frown}{WT} = 86°$ and $m\overset{\frown}{EA} = 62°$.

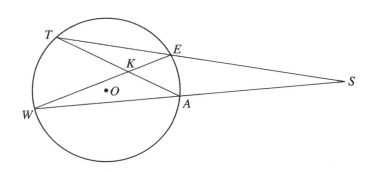

21. Find $m\angle EWA$.

22. Find $m\angle WET$.

23. Find $m\angle WES$.

24. Find $m\angle WST$.

In $\odot O$, $m\angle EWA = 36°$ and $m\angle WST = 42°$.

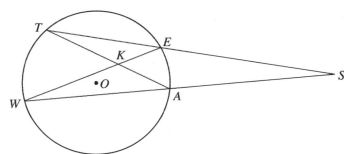

25. Find $m\angle WES$.

26. Find $m\overset{\frown}{TW}$.

27. Find $m\overset{\frown}{EA}$.

28. Find $m\angle TKE$.

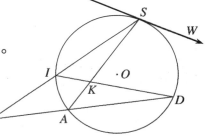

29. In the figure at right, $m\overset{\frown}{SD} = 92°$, $m\overset{\frown}{DA} = 103°$, $m\overset{\frown}{AI} = 41°$ and $\overleftrightarrow{SW}$ is tangent to $\odot O$. Find $m\angle AKD$ and $m\angle VAS$.

30. In the figure at right, $m\overset{\frown}{EK} = 43°$, $\overline{EW} \cong \overline{KW}$, and $\overleftrightarrow{ST}$ is tangent to $\odot O$. Find $m\angle WEO$ and $m\angle SEW$.

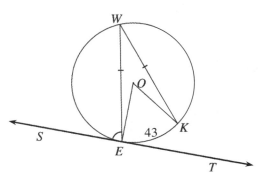

Answers

1. 38°   2. 28°   3. 28°   4. 180°   5. 114°

6. 114°   7. 246°   8. 332°   9. 68°   10. 73°

11. 98°   12. 124°   13. 50°   14. 55°   15. 18°

16. 27°   17. 55°   18. 77°   19. 35°   20. 50°

21. $\frac{1}{2}(62°) = 31°$

22. $\frac{1}{2}(86°) = 43°$

23. $180° - 43° = 137°$

24. $180° - 137° - 31° = 12°$

25. $180° - 36° - 42° = 102°$

26. $m\angle TEW = 180° - 102° = 78°, 2(78°) = 156°$

27. $2(36°) = 72°$

28. $180° - 36° - 78° = 66°$

29. $m\angle SAD = \frac{1}{2}(92°)$, $m\angle IDA = \frac{1}{2}(41°)$, $180° - 46° - 20.5° = 113.5°$, $m\angle VAS = 180° - 46° = 134°$

30. $m\angle EWK = \frac{1}{2}(43°) = 21.5°$, $m\angle EOK = 43°$, so $317°$ remain for the other angle at O. $m\angle WEO = m\angle WKO$ and for $WEOK$, $360° - 21.5° - 317° = 21.5° = m\angle WEO + m\angle WKO$, so $m\angle WEO = \frac{1}{2}(21.5°) = 10.75°$. $m\angle SEO = 90°$, $m\angle WEO = 10.75°$, so $m\angle SEW = 79.25°$.

The probability of one event occurring, knowing that a second event has already occurred is called a conditional probability. Two-way tables are useful to visualize conditional probability situations.

See the Math Notes boxes in Lessons 10.2.1 and 10.2.3.

Example 1

For the spinners at right, assume that the smaller sections of spinner #1 are half the size of the larger section and for spinner #2 assume that the smaller sections are one third the size of the larger section.

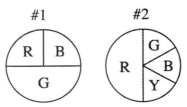

a.   Draw a diagram for spinning twice.

b.   What is the probability of getting the same color twice?

c.   If you know you got the same color twice, what is the probability it was red?

The diagram for part (a) is shown at right. Note that the boxes do not need to be to scale. The circled boxes indicate getting the same color and the total probability for part (b) is: $\frac{1}{8} + \frac{1}{12} + \frac{1}{24} = \frac{6}{24} = \frac{1}{4}$.

For part (c), both red is $\frac{1}{8}$ out of the $\frac{1}{4}$ from part (b) and so the probability the spinner was red knowing that you got the same color twice is $\frac{1}{8} \div \frac{1}{4} = \frac{1}{8} \cdot \frac{4}{1} = \frac{1}{2}$.

	$R(\frac{1}{2})$	$G(\frac{1}{6})$	$B(\frac{1}{6})$	$Y(\frac{1}{6})$
$R(\frac{1}{4})$	$\frac{1}{8}$	$\frac{1}{24}$	$\frac{1}{24}$	$\frac{1}{24}$
$B(\frac{1}{4})$	$\frac{1}{8}$	$\frac{1}{24}$	$\frac{1}{24}$	$\frac{1}{24}$
$G(\frac{1}{2})$	$\frac{1}{4}$	$\frac{1}{12}$	$\frac{1}{12}$	$\frac{1}{12}$

Example 2

A soda company conducted a taste test for three different kinds of soda that it makes. It surveyed 200 people in each age group about their favorite flavor and the results are shown in the table below.

Age	Soda A	Soda B	Soda C
Under 20	30	44	126
20 to 39	67	75	58
40 to 59	88	78	34
60 and over	141	49	10

a. What is the probability that a participant chose Soda C or was under 20 years old?

b. What is the probability that Soda A was chosen?

c. If Soda A was chosen, what is the probability that the participant was 60 years old or older?

For part (a), using the addition rule:

$P(C \text{ or } <20) = P(C) + P(<20) - P(C \text{ and } <20) = \frac{238}{800} + \frac{200}{800} - \frac{126}{800} = \frac{312}{800} = 0.39$.

For part (b), adding the participants selecting Soda A: $\frac{30+67+88+141}{800} = \frac{316}{800} = 0.395$.

For part (c), taking only the participants over 60 selecting Soda A out of all those selecting Soda A: $\frac{141}{30+67+88+141} \approx 0.43$

Problems

1. Two normal dice are thrown.

    a. How many ways are there to get 7 points?

    b. What is the probability of getting 7 points?

    c. If you got 7 points, what is the probability that one die was a 5?

2. Elizabeth and Scott are playing game at the state fair that uses two spinners which are shown in the diagrams at right. The player spins both wheels and if the colors match you win a prize.

    a. Make a probability diagram for this situation

    b. What is the probability of winning a prize?

    c. If you won a prize, what is the probability that the matching colors were red?

Spinner #1

R: $\frac{2}{3}$ B: $\frac{1}{3}$

Spinner #2

R	G
B	Y

3. The probability that it is Friday and a Sarah is absent is $\frac{1}{20}$. Since the school week has 5 days, the probability it is Friday is $\frac{1}{5}$. If today is Friday, what is the probability that Sarah is absent?

4. An airline wants to determine if passengers not checking luggage is related to people being on business trips. Data for 1000 random passengers at an airport was collected and summarized in the table below.

	Checked Baggage	No Checked Baggage
Traveling for business	103	387
Not traveling for business	216	294

    a. What is the probability of traveling and not checking baggage?

    b. If the passenger is traveling for business, what is the probability of not having checked baggage?

5. In Canada, 92% of the households have televisions. 72% of households have televisions and internet access. What is the probability that a house has internet given that it has a television?

6. There is a 25% chance that Claire will have to work tonight and cannot study for the big math test. If Claire studies, then she has an 80% chance of earning a good grade. If she does not study, she only have a 30% chance of earning a good grade.

    a. Draw a diagram to represent this situation.

    b. Calculate the probability of Claire earning a good grade on the math test.

    c. If Claire earned a good grade, what is the probability that she studied?

7. A bag contains 4 blue marbles and 2 yellow marbles. Two marbles are randomly chosen.

    a. What is the probability that both marbles are blue?

    b. What is the probability that both marbles are yellow?

    c. What is the probability of one blue and then one yellow?

    d. If you were told that both marbles selected were the same color, what is the probability that both are blue?

8. At Cal's Computer Warehouse, Cal wants to know the probability that a customer who comes into his store will buy a computer or a printer. He collected the following data during a recent week: 233 customers entered the store, 126 purchased computers, 44 purchased printers and 93 made no purchase.

   a. Draw a Venn diagram to represent the situation

   b. From this data, what is the probability that the next customer who comes into the store will buy a computer or a printer?

   c. Cal has promised a raise for his salespeople if they can increase the probability that the customers who buy computers also buy printers. For the given data, what is the probability that if a customer bought a computer, he or she also bought a printer?

9. A survey of 200 recent high school graduates found that 170 had driver licenses and 108 had jobs. Twenty-one said that they had neither a driver license nor a job.

   a. Draw a two-way table to represent the situation

   b. If one of these 200 graduates was randomly selected, what is the probability that he or she has a job and no license?

   c. If the randomly selected graduate is known to have a job, what is the probability that he or she has a license?

10. At McDougal's Giant Hotdogs 15% of the part time workers are under 18 years old. The most desirable shift is 4-8pm and 80% of those under 18 have that shift. 30% of the other part time workers have that shift.

   a. Represent these probabilities in a two-way table.

   b. What is the probability that a randomly selected part time worker is 18 or over and does not work the 4-8pm shift?

   c. What is the probability that a randomly selected 18 year old or over part time worker does not work the 4-8pm shift

Answers

1. a. 6 ways

 b. $\frac{6}{36} = \frac{1}{6}$

 c. $\frac{2}{36} \div \frac{6}{36} = \frac{1}{3}$

2. a. See diagram at right.

 b. $\frac{1}{6} + \frac{1}{12} = \frac{1}{4}$

 c. $\frac{1}{6} \div \frac{1}{4} = \frac{2}{3}$

	$R(\frac{1}{4})$	$B(\frac{1}{4})$	$G(\frac{1}{4})$	$Y(\frac{1}{4})$
$R(\frac{2}{3})$	$\frac{1}{6}$	$\frac{1}{6}$	$\frac{1}{6}$	$\frac{1}{6}$
$B(\frac{1}{3})$	$\frac{1}{12}$	$\frac{1}{12}$	$\frac{1}{12}$	$\frac{1}{12}$

3. $\frac{1}{20} \div \frac{1}{5} = \frac{1}{4}$

4. a. $\frac{681}{1000} = 0.681$

 b. $\frac{387}{103+387} \approx 0.79$

5. $\frac{72\%}{92\%} \approx 78\%$

6. a. See diagram at right.

 b. $0.075 + 0.60 = 0.675 = 67.5\%$

 c. $\frac{0.60}{0.675} \approx 0.89$

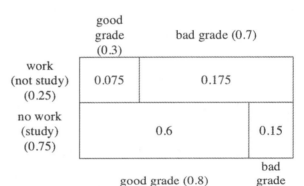

7. a. $\frac{4}{6} \cdot \frac{3}{5} = \frac{2}{5}$

 b. $\frac{2}{6} \cdot \frac{1}{5} = \frac{1}{15}$

 c. $\frac{4}{6} \cdot \frac{2}{5} = \frac{4}{15}$

 d. $\frac{2}{5} \div (\frac{2}{5} + \frac{1}{15}) = \frac{6}{7}$

8. a.

 b. $\frac{140}{233}$

 c. $\frac{41}{126}$

9. a. See diagram at right.

 b. $\frac{9}{200}$

 c. $\frac{99}{108}$

	Job	No Job	
License	99	71	170
No Lic.	9	21	30
	108	92	200

10. a. See diagram at right.

 b. 0.79

 c. $\frac{0.79}{0.85} \approx 0.93$

	4–8pm	other	
<18	(.15)(.80)=0.12	0.03	0.15
≥18	(.3)(.2)=0.06	0.79	0.85
	0.18	0.82	1

Students take on challenging problems using the Fundamental Principle of Counting, permutations, and combinations to compute probabilities. These techniques are essential when the sample space is too large to model or to count.

See the Math Notes boxes in Lessons 10.3.1, 10.3.2, 10.3.3, and 10.3.5.

Example 1

Twenty-three people have entered the pie-eating contest at the county fair. The first place pie-eater (the person eating the most pies in fifteen minutes) wins a pie each week for a year. Second place will receive new baking ware to make his/her own pies, and third place will receive the *Sky High Pies* recipe book. How many different possible top finishers are there?

Since the prizes are different for first, second, and third place, the order of the top finishers matters. We can use a decision chart to determine the number of ways we can have winners. How many different people can come in first? Twenty-three. Once first place is "chosen" (i.e., removed from the list of contenders) how many people are left to take second place? Twenty-two. This leaves twenty-one possible third place finishers. Just as with the branches on the tree diagram, multiply these numbers to determine the number of arrangements: (23)(22)(21) = 10,626.

$$\underset{\text{First}}{\underline{23}} \quad \underset{\text{Second}}{\underline{22}} \quad \underset{\text{Third}}{\underline{21}}$$

Example 2

Fifteen students are participating in a photo-shoot for a layout in the new journal *Mathmaticious*. In how many ways can you arrange:

a. Eight of them? b. Two of them? c. Fifteen of them?

We can use a decision chart for each of these situations, but there is another, more efficient method for answering these questions. An arrangement of items where order matters is called a **permutation**, and in this case, since changing the order of the students changes the layout, the order matters.

With a permutation, you need to know the total number things to be arranged (in this case $n = 15$ students) and how many will be taken (r) at a time. The formula for a permutation is $_nP_r = \frac{n!}{(n-r)!}$.

In part (a), we have 15 students taken 8 at a time.
The number of permutations is: $_{15}P_8 = \frac{15!}{(15-8)!} = \frac{15!}{7!} = 15 \cdot 14 \cdot 13 \cdot 12 \cdot 11 \cdot 10 \cdot 9 \cdot 8 = 259,459,200$

In part (b) the solution becomes: $_{15}P_2 = \frac{15!}{(15-2)!} = \frac{15!}{13!} = 15 \cdot 14 = 210$

Part (c) poses a new problem: $_{15}P_{15} = \frac{15!}{(15-15)!} = \frac{15!}{0!}$

What is $0!$? "Factorial" means to calculate the product of the integers from the given value down to one. How can we compute $0!$? If it equals zero, we have a problem because part (c) would not have an answer (dividing by zero is undefined). But this situation must have an answer. In fact, if we used a decision chart to determine how many ways the 15 people can line up, we would find that there are 15! arrangements. Therefore, if $_{15}P_{15} = 15!$ and $0! = 1$. This is another case of mathematicians defining elements of mathematics to fit their needs. $0!$ is defined to equal 1 so that other mathematics makes sense.

Example 3

In the annual homecoming parade, three students get to ride on the lead float. Seven students are being considered for this coveted position. How many ways can three students be chosen for this honor?

All three students who are selected will ride on the lead float, but whether they are the first, second, or third student selected does not matter. In a case where the order of the selections does not matter, the situation is called a **combination**. This means that if the students were labeled A, B, C, D, E, and F, choosing A, B, and then C would be essentially the same as choosing B, C, and then A. In fact, all the arrangements of A, B, and C could be lumped together. This makes the number of combinations much smaller than the number of permutations. The symbol for a combination is $_nC_r$ where n is the total number of items under consideration, and r is the number of items we will choose. It is often read as "n choose r." In this problem we have $_7C_3$, 7 choose 3. The formula is similar to the formula for a permutation, but we must divide out the similar groups.

$$_nC_r = \frac{n!}{(n-r)!r!}$$

Here we have: $_7C_3 = \frac{7!}{(7-3)!3!} = \frac{7!}{4!3!} = \frac{7 \cdot 6 \cdot 5 \cdot 4 \cdot 3 \cdot 2 \cdot 1}{4 \cdot 3 \cdot 2 \cdot 1 \cdot 3 \cdot 2 \cdot 1} = 35$

Problems

Simplify the following expressions.

1. 10!

2. $\frac{10!}{3!}$

3. $\frac{35!}{30!}$

4. $\frac{88!}{87!}$

5. $\frac{72!}{70!}$

6. $\frac{65!}{62!3!}$

7. $_8P_2$

8. $_{15}P_0$

9. $_9P_9$

10. $_{12}C_4$

11. $_5C_0$

12. $_{32}C_{32}$

Solve the following problems.

13. How many ways can you arrange the letters from the word "KAREN"?

14. How many ways can you arrange the letters from the word "KAREN" if you want the arrangement to begin with a vowel?

15. All standard license plates in Alaska start with three letters followed by three digits. If repetition is allowed, how many different license plates are there?

16. For \$3.99, The Creamery Ice Cream Parlor will put any three different flavored scoops, out of their 25 flavors of ice cream, into a bowl. How many different "bowls" are there? (Note: A bowl of chocolate, strawberry, and vanilla is the same bowl as a bowl of chocolate, vanilla, and strawberry.)

17. Suppose those same three scoops of ice cream are on a cone. Now how many arrangements are there? (Note: Ice cream on a cone must be eaten "top down" because you cannot eat the bottom or middle scoop out, keeping the cone intact.)

18. A normal deck of playing cards contains 52 cards. How many five-card poker hands can be made?

19. How many ways are there to make a full house (three of one kind, two of another)?

20. What is the probability of getting a full house (three of one kind of card and two of another)? Assume a standard deck and no wild cards.

For problems 21–25, a bag contains 36 marbles. There are twelve blue marbles, eight red marbles, seven green marbles, five yellow marbles, and four white marbles. Without looking, you reach into the bag and pull out eight marbles. What is the probability you pull out:

21. All blue marbles?

22. Four blue and four white marbles?

23. Seven green and one yellow marble?

24. At least one red and at least two yellow?

25. No blue marbles?

Answers

1. 3,628,800

2. 604,800

3. 38,955,840

4. 88

5. 5,112

6. 43,680

7. 56

8. 1

9. 362,880

10. 495

11. 1

12. 1

13. $5! = 120$

14. $2(4!) = 48$

15. $(26)(26)(26)(10)(10)(10) = 17,576,000$

16. $_{25}C_3 = 2300$

17. $_{25}P_3 = 13,800$ (On a cone, order matters!)

18. $_{52}C_5 = 2,598,960$

19. This is tricky and tough! There are 13 different "types" of cards: twos, threes, fours, ..., Jacks, Queens, Kings, and Aces. We need to choose which of the 13 we want three of $(_{13}C_1)$. Once we choose what type (for example, we pick Jacks) then we need to choose which three out of the four to take $(_4C_3)$. Then from the remaining 12 types, we choose which type to have two of $(_{12}C_1)$. Then again we need to choose which two out of the four $(_4C_2)$. This gives us $(_{13}C_1) \cdot (_4C_3) \cdot (_{12}C_1) \cdot (_4C_2) = 3,744$.

20. We already calculated the numbers we need in problems 18 and 19 so: $\frac{3,744}{2,598,960} \approx 0.0014$.

21. Each time we reach in and pull out 8 marbles, order does not matter. The number of ways to do this is $_{36}C_8$. This is the number in the sample space, i.e., the denominator. How many ways can we pull out all blue? $_{12}C_8$. Therefore the probability is $\frac{_{12}C_8}{_{36}C_8} \approx 0.0000164$.

22. Same denominator. Now we want to choose 4 from the 12 blue, $_{12}C_4$, and 4 from the 4 whites, $_4C_4$. $\frac{_{12}C_4 \cdot _4C_4}{_{36}C_8} \approx 0.0000164$, the same answer!

23. Seven green: $_7C_7$, one yellow: $_5C_1$. $\frac{_7C_7 \cdot _5C_1}{_{36}C_8} \approx 0.0000001652$

24. Here we have to get at least one red: $_8C_1$, and at least two yellow: $_5C_2$, but the other five marbles can come from the rest of the pot: $_{33}C_5$. Therefore, $\frac{_8C_1 \cdot _5C_2 \cdot _{33}C_5}{_{36}C_8} \approx 0.627$.

25. To get no blue marbles means we want all eight from the other 24 non-blue marbles. $\frac{_{24}C_8}{_{36}C_8} \approx 0.0243$.

Students have already worked with solids, finding the volume and surface area of prisms and other shapes built with blocks. Now these skills are extended to finding the volumes and surface areas of pyramids, cones, and spheres.

See the Math Notes boxes in Lessons 11.1.2, 11.1.3, 11.1.4, 11.1.5, and 11.2.2.

Example 1

A regular hexahedron has an edge length of 20 cm. What are the surface area and volume of this solid?

Although the name "regular hexahedron" might sound intimidating, it just refers to a regular solid with six (hexa) faces. As defined earlier, regular means all angles are congruent and all side lengths are congruent. A regular hexahedron is just a cube, so all six faces are congruent squares.

To find the volume of the cube, we can use our previous knowledge: multiply the area of the base by the height. Since the base is a square, its area is 400 square cm. The height is 20 cm, therefore the volume is (400)(20) = 8000 cubic cm.

To calculate the surface area we will find the sum of the areas of all six faces. Since each face is a square and they are all congruent, this will be fairly easy. The area of one square is 400 square cm, and there are six of them. Therefore the surface area is 2400 square cm.

Example 2

The base of the pyramid at right is a regular hexagon. Using the measurements provided, calculate the surface area and volume of the pyramid.

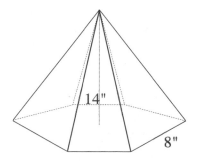

The volume of any pyramid is $V = \frac{1}{3} A_b h$ (h is the height of the pyramid and A_b is the area of the base). We calculate the surface area the same way we do for all solids: find the area of each face and base, then add them all together. The lateral faces of the pyramid are all congruent triangles. The base is a regular hexagon. Since we need the area of the hexagon for both the volume and the surface area, we will find it first.

There are several ways to find the area of a regular hexagon. One way is to cut the hexagon into six congruent equilateral triangles, each with a side of 8". If we can find the area of one triangle, then we can multiply by 6 to find the area of the hexagon. To find the area of one triangle we need to find the value of h, the height of the triangle. Recall that we studied these triangles earlier; remember that the height cuts the equilateral triangle into two congruent 30°-60°-90° triangles. To find h, we can use the Pythagorean Theorem, or if you remember the pattern for a 30°-60°-90° triangle, we can use that. With either method we find that $h = 4\sqrt{3}$". Therefore the area of one equilateral triangle is shown at right.

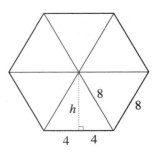

$$A = \tfrac{1}{2}bh$$
$$= \tfrac{1}{2} \cdot (8) \cdot \left(4\sqrt{3}\right)$$
$$= 16\sqrt{3} \approx 27.71 \text{ in.}^2$$

The area of the hexagon is $6 \cdot 16\sqrt{3} = 96\sqrt{3} \approx 166.28$ in.^{2}. Now find the volume of the pyramid using the formula as shown at right.

$$V = \tfrac{1}{3}A_b h$$
$$= \tfrac{1}{3} \cdot \left(96\sqrt{3}\right) \cdot (14)$$
$$= 448\sqrt{3} \approx 776 \text{ in.}^3$$

Next we need to find the area of one of the triangular faces. These triangles are slanted, and the height of one of them is called a slant height. The problem does not give us the value of the slant height (labeled c at right), but we can calculate it based on the information we already have.

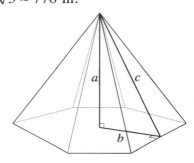

A cross section of the pyramid at right shows a right triangle in its interior. One leg is labeled a, another b, and the hypotenuse c. The original picture gives us $a = 14$". The length of b we found previously: it is the height of one of the equilateral triangles in the hexagonal base. Therefore, $b = 4\sqrt{3}$". To calculate c, we use the Pythagorean Theorem.

$$a^2 + b^2 = c^2$$
$$14^2 + (4\sqrt{3})^2 = c^2$$
$$196 + 48 = c^2$$
$$c^2 = 244$$
$$c = \sqrt{244} = 2\sqrt{61} \approx 15.62 \text{ "}$$

The base of one of the slanted triangles is 8", the length of the side of the hexagon. Therefore the area of one slanted triangle is $8\sqrt{61} \approx 62.48$ in.^{2} as shown below right.

$$A = \tfrac{1}{2} \cdot b \cdot h$$
$$= \tfrac{1}{2} \cdot (8) \cdot \left(2\sqrt{61}\right)$$
$$= 8\sqrt{61} \approx 62.48 \text{ in.}^2$$

Since there are six of these triangles, the area of the lateral faces is $6(8\sqrt{61}) = 48\sqrt{61} \approx 374.89$ in.^{2}.

Now we have all we need to find the total surface area: $96\sqrt{3} + 48\sqrt{61} \approx 541.17$ in.^{2}.

Example 3

The cone at right has the measurements shown. What are the lateral surface area and volume of the cone?

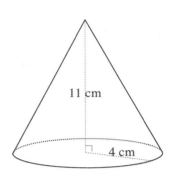

The volume of a cone is the same as the volume of any pyramid: $V = \frac{1}{3} A_b h$. The only difference is that the base is a circle, but since we know how to find the area of a circle ($A = \pi r^2$), we find the volume as shown at right.

$$V = \frac{1}{3} A_b h$$
$$= \frac{1}{3} \left(\pi r^2 \right) h$$
$$= \frac{1}{3} \left(\pi \cdot 4^2 \right) \cdot 11$$
$$= \frac{1}{3} \cdot (176\pi) = \frac{176\pi}{3}$$
$$\approx 184.3 \text{ cm}^3$$

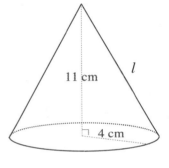

Calculating the lateral surface area of a cone is a different matter. If we think of a cone as a child's party hat, we can imagine cutting it apart to make it lay flat. If we did, we would find that the cone is really a sector of a circle – not the circle that makes up the base of the cone, but a circle whose radius is the slant height of the cone. By using ratios we can come up with the formula for the lateral surface area of the cone, $SA = \pi r l$, where r is the radius of the base and l is the slant height. In this problem, we have r, but we do not have l. Find it by taking a cross section of the cone to create a right triangle. The legs of the right triangle are 11 cm and 4 cm, and l is the hypotenuse. Using the Pythagorean Theorem we can calculate $l \approx 11.7$ cm, as shown below right.

$$4^2 + 11^2 = l^2$$
$$16 + 121 = l^2$$
$$l^2 = 137$$
$$l = \sqrt{137} \approx 11.7 \text{ cm}$$

Now we can calculate the lateral surface area:
$SA = \pi(4)(11.7) \approx 147.1 \text{ cm}^2$

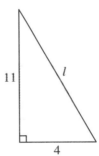

Example 4

The sphere at right has a radius of 6 feet. Calculate the surface area and the volume of the sphere.

Since spheres are related to circles, we should expect that the formulas for the surface area and volume will have π in them. The surface area of a sphere with radius r is $4\pi r^2$. Since we know the radius of the sphere is 6, $SA = 4\pi(6)^2 = 144\pi \approx 452.39 \text{ ft}^2$. To find the volume of the sphere, we use the formula $V = \frac{4}{3} \pi r^3$. Therefore, $V = \frac{4}{3} \pi(6)^3 = \frac{4 \cdot 216 \cdot \pi}{3} = 288\pi \approx 904.78 \text{ ft}^3$.

Problems

1. The figure at right is a square based pyramid. Calculate its surface area and its volume.

9 cm 7 cm

2. Another pyramid, congruent to the one in the previous problem, is glued to the bottom of the first pyramid, so that their bases coincide. What is the name of the new solid? Calculate the surface area and volume of the new solid.

3. A regular pentagon has a side length of 10 in. Calculate the area of the pentagon.

4. The pentagon of the previous problem is the base of a right pyramid with a height of 18 in. What is the surface area and volume of the pyramid?

5 ft
12 ft

5. What is the total surface area and volume of the cone at right?

6. A cone fits perfectly inside a cylinder as shown. If the volume of the cylinder is 81π cubic units, what is the volume of the cone?

7. A sphere has a radius of 12 cm. What are the surface area and volume of the sphere?

Find the volume of each figure.

8.
3 m
4 m
4 m

9.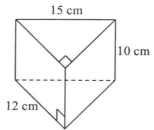
15 cm
10 cm
12 cm

10.
36 ft
36 ft
40 ft
25 ft

11.
2 in.
3.5 in.

12.
12.1 m
6.3 m

13.
2 m
5 m

14.

9 ft

2 ft

4 ft

15.

11 cm

11 cm

16.

8 cm

4 cm $2\sqrt{3}$

17.

8 in

10 in

12 in

18.

13 in

5 in

19.

11 cm

8 cm

20.

1.0 m

2.6 m

21.

10 in.

16 in.

16 in.

22.

11 m

18 m

23.

6.1 cm

6.2 cm

8.3 cm

24.

5 cm

2 cm

25.

7 in.

8 in.

8 in.

26. Find the volume of the solid shown.

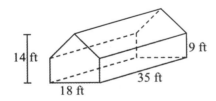

14 ft

9 ft

35 ft

18 ft

27. Find the volume of the remaining solid after a hole with a diameter of 4 mm is drilled through it.

15 mm

8 mm

10 mm

Find the total surface area of the figures in the previous volume problems.

28. Problem 1   29. Problem 2   30. Problem 3   31. Problem 5

32. Problem 6   33. Problem 7   34. Problem 8   35. Problem 9

36. Problem 10   37. Problem 14   38. Problem 18   39. Problem 19

Use the given information to find the volume of the cone.

40. radius = 1.5 in.
    height = 4 in.

41. diameter = 6 cm
    height = 5 cm

42. base area = 25π
    height = 3

43. base circum. = 12π
    height = 10

44. diameter = 12
    slant height = 10

45. lateral area = 12π
    radius = 1.5

Use the given information to find the lateral area of the cone.

46. radius = 8 in.
    slant height = 1.75 in.

47. slant height = 10 cm
    height = 8 cm

48. base area = 25π
    slant height = 6

49. radius = 8 cm
    height = 15 cm

50. volume = 100π
    height = 5

51. volume = 36π
    radius = 3

Use the given information to find the volume of the sphere.

52. radius = 10 cm

53. diameter = 10 cm

54. circumference of
    great circle = 12π

55. surface area = 256π

56. circumference of
    great circle = 20 cm

57. surface area = 100

Use the given information to find the surface area of the sphere.

58. radius = 5 in.

59. diameter = 12 in.

60. circumference of
    great circle = 14

61. volume = 250

62. circumference of
    great circle = π

63. volume = $\frac{9\pi}{2}$

Answers

1. $V = 147$ cm^3, $SA \approx 184.19$ cm^2

2. Octahedron, $V = 294$ cm^3, $SA \approx 270.38$ cm^2

3. $A \approx 172.05$ in.^{2}

4. $V = 1032.29$ in.^{3}, $SA \approx 653.75$ in.^{2}

5. $V \approx 314.16$ ft^3, $SA = 90\pi \approx 282.74$ ft^2

6. 27π cubic units

7. $SA = 576\pi \approx 1089.56$ cm^2, $V = 2304\pi \approx 7238.23$ cm^3

8. 48 m^3

9. 540 cm^3

10. 14966.6 ft^3

11. 76.9 m^3

12. 1508.75 m^3

13. 157 m^3

14. 72 ft^3

15. 1045.4 cm^3

16. 332.6 cm^3

17. 320 in.^{3}

18. 314.2 in.^{3}

19. 609.7 cm^3

20. 2.5 m^3

21. 512 m^3

22. 514.4 m^3

23. 2.3 cm^3

24. 20.9 cm^3

25. 149.3 in.^{3}

26. 7245 ft^3

27. 1011.6 mm^3

28. 80 m^2

29. 468 cm^2

30. 3997.33 ft^2

31. 727.98 m^2

32. $50\pi + 20\pi \approx 219.8$ m^2

33. 124 ft^2

34. $121\pi + 189.97 \approx 569.91$ cm^2

35. $192 + 48\sqrt{3} \approx 275.14$ cm^2

36. 213.21 in.^{2}

37. 576 in.^{2}

38. 193.0 in.^{2}

39. 2394.69 ft^2

40. $3\pi \approx 9.42$ in.^{3}

41. $15\pi \approx 47.12$ cm^3

42. $25\pi \approx 78.54$ units^3

43. $120\pi \approx 376.99$ units^3

44. $96\pi \approx 301.59$ units^3

45. ≈ 18.51 units^3

46. $14\pi \approx 43.98$ in.^{2}

47. $60\pi \approx 188.50$ cm^2

48. $30\pi \approx 94.25$ units^2

49. $136\pi \approx 427.26$ cm^2

50. ≈ 224.35 units^2

51. 116.58 units^2

52. $\frac{4000\pi}{3} \approx 4188.79$ cm^3

53. $\frac{500\pi}{3} \approx 523.60$ cm^3

54. $288\pi \approx 904.79$ units^3

55. $\frac{2048\pi}{3} \approx 2144.66$ units^3

56. ≈ 135.09 units^3

57. ≈ 94.03 units^3

58. $100\pi \approx 314.16$ units^2

59. $144\pi \approx 452.39$ untis^2

60. ≈ 62.39 units^2

61. ≈ 191.91 units^2

62. $\pi \approx 3.14$ units^2

63. $9\pi \approx 28.27$ units^2

Throughout the year, students have varied their study between two-dimensional objects to three-dimensional objects. This section applies these studies to geometry on a globe. Students learn terms associated with a globe (longitude, latitude, equator, great circle), how the globe is divided, and how to locate cities on it. Additionally, they can find the distance between two cities with the same latitude. Students also notice that some of the facts that are true on flat surfaces change on a curved surface. For instance, it is possible to have a triangle with two right angles on a sphere.

Example 1

If Annapolis, Maryland is at approximately 75° west of prime meridian, and 38° north of the equator, and Sacramento, California is approximately 122° west of prime meridian, and 38° north of the equator, approximate the distance between the two cities. (The Earth's radius is approximately 4000 miles.)

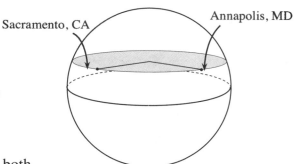

The two cities lie on the same latitude, so they are both on the circumference of the shaded circle. The central angle that connects the two cities is $122° - 75° = 47°$. This means that the arc length between the two cities is $\frac{47}{360}$ of the circle's circumference. To find the shaded circle's circumference, we must find the radius of the shaded circle.

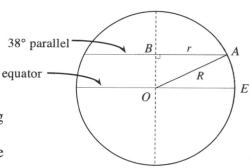

Looking at a cross section of the globe we see something familiar: triangles. In the diagram R is the radius of the Earth while r is the radius of the shaded circle. Since the shaded circle is at 38° north, $m\angle EOA = 38°$. Because the latitude lines are parallel, we also know that $m\angle BAO = 38°$.

$$\cos 38° = \frac{r}{R}$$

We use trigonometry to solve for r, as shown at right. This is the radius of the circle on which the two cities lie. Next we find the fraction of its circumference that is the distance, D, between the two cities.

$$\cos 38° = \frac{r}{4000}$$
$$r = 4000 \cos 38°$$
$$r \approx 3152$$

Therefore the cities are approximately 2586 miles apart.

$$D = \tfrac{47}{360}\left(2 \cdot \pi \cdot r\right)$$
$$= \tfrac{47}{360}\left(2 \cdot \pi \cdot 3152\right)$$
$$\approx 2586 \text{ miles}$$

Problems

1. Lisbon, Portugal is also 38° north of the equator, but it is 9° west of the prime meridian. How far is Annapolis, MD from Lisbon?

2. How far is Sacramento, CA from Lisbon?

3. Port Elizabeth, South Africa is about 32° south of the equator and 25° east of the prime meridian. Perth, Australia is also about 32° south, but 115° east of the prime meridian. How far apart are Port Elizabeth and Perth?

Answers

1. ≈ 3631 miles.

2. ≈ 6216 miles

3. ≈ 5328 miles

In this lesson, students consider lengths of segments and measures of angles formed
when tangents and secants intersect inside and outside of a circle. Recall that a tangent is
a line that intersects the circle at exactly one point. A secant is a line that intersects the
circle at two points. As before, the explanations and justifications for the concepts are
dependent on triangles.

See the Math Notes box in Lesson 11.2.3.

Example 1

In the circle at right, $m\widehat{IY} = 60°$ and $m\widehat{NE} = 40°$. What is $m\angle IPY$?

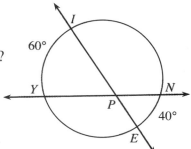

The two lines, $\overleftrightarrow{IE}$ and $\overleftrightarrow{YN}$, are secants since they each intersect
the circle at two points. When two secants intersect in the
interior of the circle, the measures of the angles formed are each
one-half the sum of the measures of the intercepted arcs. Hence
$m\angle IPY = \frac{1}{2}(m\widehat{IY} + m\widehat{NE})$ since $\widehat{IY}$ and $\widehat{NE}$ are the intercepted
arcs for this angle. Therefore:

$$m\angle IPY = \tfrac{1}{2}(m\widehat{IY} + m\widehat{NE})$$
$$= \tfrac{1}{2}(60° + 40°)$$
$$= 50°$$

Example 2

In the circle at right, $m\widehat{OA} = 140°$ and $m\widehat{RH} = 32°$. What is $m\angle OCA$?

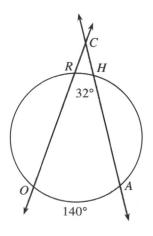

This time the secants intersect outside the circle at point C. When
this happens, the measure of the angle is one-half the difference of
the measures of the intercepted arcs. Therefore:

$$m\angle OCA = \tfrac{1}{2}(m\widehat{OA} - m\widehat{RH})$$
$$= \tfrac{1}{2}(140° - 32°)$$
$$= 54°$$

Example 3

$\overrightarrow{MI}$ and $\overrightarrow{MK}$ are tangent to the circle. $m\overset{\frown}{ILK} = 199°$ and $MI = 13$. Calculate $m\overset{\frown}{IK}$, $m\angle IMK$, and the length of $\overline{MK}$.

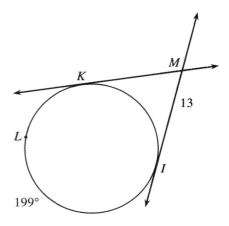

When tangents intersect a circle we have a similar result as we did with the secants. Here, the measure of the angle is again one-half the difference of the measures of the intercepted arcs. But before we can find the measure of the angle, we first need to find $m\overset{\frown}{IK}$. Remember that there are a total of 360° in a circle, and here the circle is broken into just two arcs. If $m\overset{\frown}{ILK} = 199°$, then $m\overset{\frown}{IK} = 360° - 199° = 161°$. Now we can find $m\angle IMK$ by following the steps shown at right.

$$m\angle IMK = \tfrac{1}{2}(m\overset{\frown}{ILK} - m\overset{\frown}{IK})$$
$$= \tfrac{1}{2}(199° - 161°)$$
$$= 19°$$

Lastly, when two tangents intersect, the segments from the point of intersection to the point of tangency are congruent. Therefore, $MK = 13$.

Example 4

In the figure at right, $DO = 20$, $NO = 6$, and $NU = 8$. Calculate the length of $\overline{UT}$.

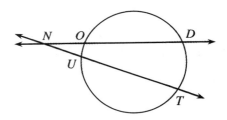

We have already looked at what happens when secants intersect inside the circle. (We did this when we considered the lengths of parts of intersecting chords. The chord was just a portion of the secant. See the Math Notes box in Lesson 10.1.4.) Now we have the secants intersecting outside the circle. When this happens, we can write $NO \cdot ND = NU \cdot NT$. In this example, we do not know the length of $\overline{UT}$, but we do know that $NT = NU + UT$. Therefore we can write and solve the equation at right.

$$NO \cdot ND = NU \cdot NT$$
$$6 \cdot (6 + 20) = 8 \cdot (8 + UT)$$
$$156 = 64 + 8UT$$
$$92 = 8UT$$
$$UT = 11.5$$

Problems

In each circle, C is the center and $\overline{AB}$ is tangent to the circle point B. Find the area of each circle.

1. $\overline{AC} = 30$

2.

$\overline{AC} = 45$

3.

4.

5.

$\overline{AC} = 16$

6. $\overline{AC} = 86$

7.

$\overline{AC} = 90$

8.

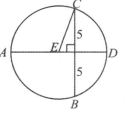

$\overline{AD} = 18$

9. In the figure at right, point E is the center and $m\angle CED = 55°$. What is the area of the circle?

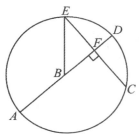

In the following problems, B is the center of the circle. Find the length of $\overline{BF}$ given the lengths below.

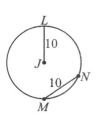

10. $EC = 14, AB = 16$

11. $EC = 35, AB = 21$

12. $FD = 5, EF = 10$

13. $EF = 9, FD = 6$

14. In $\odot R$, if $AB = 2x - 7$ and $CD = 5x - 22$, find x.

15. In $\odot O$, $\overline{MN} \cong \overline{PQ}$, $MN = 7x + 13$, and $PQ = 10x - 8$. Find PS.

16. In $\odot D$, if $AD = 5$ and $TB = 2$, find AT.

17. In $\odot J$, radius JL and chord MN have lengths of 10 cm. Find the distance from J to $\overline{MN}$.

18. In $\odot O$, $OC = 13$ and $OT = 5$. Find AB.

19. If $\overline{AC}$ is tangent to circle E and $\overline{EH} \perp \overline{GI}$, is $\triangle GEH \sim \triangle AEB$? Prove your answer.

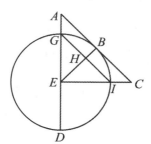

20. If $\overline{EH}$ bisects $\overline{GI}$ and $\overline{AC}$ is tangent to circle E at point B, are $\overline{AC}$ and $\overline{GI}$ parallel? Prove your answer.

Compute the value of x.

21.

22.

23.

24.

In $\odot F$, $m\overset{\frown}{AB} = 84°$, $m\overset{\frown}{BC} = 38°$, $m\overset{\frown}{CD} = 64°$, $m\overset{\frown}{DE} = 60°$. Find the measure of each angle and arc.

25. $m\overset{\frown}{EA}$

26. $m\overset{\frown}{AEB}$

27. $m\angle 1$

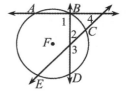

28. $m\angle 2$

29. $m\angle 3$

30. $m\angle 4$

31. If $m\overset{\frown}{ADC} = 212°$, what is $m\angle AEC$?

32. If $m\overset{\frown}{AB} = 47°$ and $m\angle AED = 47°$, what is $m\overset{\frown}{AD}$?

33. If $m\overset{\frown}{ADC} = 3 \cdot m\overset{\frown}{AC}$ what is $m\angle AEC$?

34. If $m\overset{\frown}{AB} = 60°$, $m\overset{\frown}{AD} = 130°$, and $m\overset{\frown}{DC} = 110°$, what is $m\angle DEC$?

35. If $\overleftrightarrow{RN}$ is a tangent, $RO = 3$, and $RC = 12$, what is the length of $\overline{RN}$?

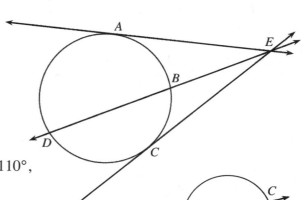

36. If $\overrightarrow{RN}$ is a tangent, $RC = 4x$, $RO = x$, and $RN = 6$, what is the length of $\overline{RC}$?

37. If $\overrightarrow{LT}$ is a tangent, $LU = 16$, $LN = 5$, and $LA = 6$, what are the lengths of $\overline{LW}$ and $\overline{NU}$?

38. If $\overrightarrow{TY}$ is a tangent, $BT = 20$, $UT = 4$, and $AT = 6$, what is the length of $\overline{EA}$ and $\overline{BE}$?

Answers

1. 275π sq. units

2. 1881π sq. units

3. 36π sq. units

4. 324π sq. units

5. 112π sq. units

6. 4260π sq. units

7. 7316π sq. units

8. 49π sq. units

9. ≈ 117.047 sq. units

10. ≈ 14.4

11. ≈ 11.6

12. ≈ 7.5

13. 3.75

14. 5

15. 31

16. 4

17. $5\sqrt{3}$ cm

18. 24

19. Yes, $\angle GEH \cong \angle AEB$ (reflexive). $\overline{EB}$ is perpendicular to $\overline{AC}$ since it is tangent so $\angle GHE \cong \angle ABE$ because all right angles are congruent. So the triangles are similar by AA~.

20. Yes. Since $\overline{EH}$ bisects $\overline{GI}$ it is also perpendicular to it (SSS). Since $\overline{AC}$ is a tangent, $\angle ABE$ is a right angle. So the lines are parallel since the corresponding angles are right angles and all right angles are equal.

21. 160

22. 9

23. 42

24. 70

25. 114

26. 276

27. 87

28. 49

29. 131

30. 38

31. 32°

32. 141°

33. 90°

34. 25°

35. 6

36. 12

37. $LW = \frac{40}{3}$ and $NU = 11$

38. $EA = \frac{22}{3}$ and $BE = \frac{20}{3}$

Students have examined the parts of circles, found measurements of their circumferences areas, chords, secants, tangents, arcs, and angles, and have used circles with probability and expected value. This section places the circle on a coordinate graph so that the students can derive the equation of a circle.

See the Math Notes box in Lesson 12.1.3.

Example 1

What is the equation of the circle centered at the origin with a radius of 5 units?

The key to deriving the equation of this circle is the Pythagorean Theorem. That means we will need to create a right triangle within the circle. First, draw the circle on graph paper, then choose any point on the circle. We do not know the exact coordinates of this point so call it (x, y). Since endpoints of the radius are $(0, 0)$ and (x, y), we can represent the length of the vertical leg as y and the length of the horizontal leg as x. If we call the radius r, then using the Pythagorean Theorem we can write $x^2 + y^2 = r^2$. Since we know the radius is 5, we can write the equation of this circle as $x^2 + y^2 = 5^2$, or $x^2 + y^2 = 25$.

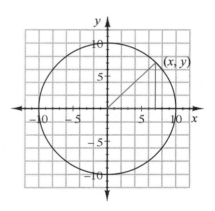

Example 2

Graph the circle $(x - 4)^2 + (y + 2)^2 = 49$.

Based on what we have seen, this is a circle with a radius of 7. This one, however, is not centered at the origin. The general equation of a circle is $(x - h)^2 + (y - k)^2 = r^2$. The center of the circle is represented by (h, k), so in this example the center is $(4, -2)$. The center of this circle has been shifted 4 units right, and 2 units down.

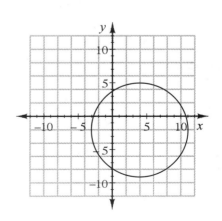

Example 3

What are the center and the radius of the circle $x^2 - 6x + y^2 + 2y - 5 = 0$?

This circle is not in the graphing form, $(x - h)^2 + (y - k)^2 = r^2$, so it is necessary to "complete the square." To make a perfect square for x we need to add 9 units and to make a perfect square for y we need to add 1 unit. Adding 10 to the right side will balance this.

Finally factor and the graphing form is achieved.

$$x^2 - 6x + y^2 + 2y - 5 = 0$$
$$(x^2 - 6x + 9) + (y^2 + 2y + 1) - 5 = 10$$
$$(x - 3)^2 + (y + 1)^2 = 15$$

The center is $(3, -1)$ and the radius is $\sqrt{15}$.

Problems

1. What is the equation of the circle centered at $(0, 0)$ with a radius of 25?

2. What is the equation of the circle centered at the origin with a radius of 7.5?

3. What is the equation of the circle centered at $(5, -3)$ with a radius of 9?

Graph the following circles.

4. $\left(x + 1\right)^2 + \left(y + 5\right)^2 = 16$

5. $x^2 + \left(y - 6\right)^2 = 36$

6. $\left(x - 3\right)^2 + y^2 = 64$

"Complete the square" to convert the equation of each circle to graphing form. Identify the center and the radius.

7. $x^2 + 6x + y^2 - 4y = -9$

8. $x^2 + 10x + y^2 - 8y = -31$

9. $x^2 - 2x + y^2 + 4y - 11 = 0$

10. $x^2 + 9x + y^2 = 0$

Answers

1. $x^2 + y^2 = 625$

2. $x^2 + y^2 = 56.25$

3. $(x-5)^2 + (y+3)^2 = 81$

4.

5.

6.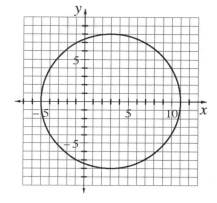

7. $(x+3)^2 + (y-2)^2 = 4; (-3,2),\ r = 2$

8. $(x+5)^2 + (y-4)^2 = 10; (-5,4), r = \sqrt{10}$

9. $(x-1)^2 + (y+2)^2 = 16; (1,-2), r = 4$

10. $(x+\frac{9}{2})^2 + y^2 = \frac{81}{4}; (-\frac{9}{2},0), r = \frac{9}{2}$

Slope is a number that indicates the steepness (or flatness) of a line, as well as its direction (up or down) left to right. It is determined by the ratio $\frac{\text{vertical change}}{\text{horizontal change}}$ between *any* two points on a line.

For lines that slope upward from left to right, the sign of the slope is **positive**. For lines that slope downward from left to right, the sign of the slope is **negative**.

Any linear equation written as $y = mx + b$, where m and b are any real numbers, is said to be in **Slope-Intercept form**. m is the slope of the line. b is the **y-intercept**, that is, the point $(0, b)$ is where the line intersects (crosses) the y-axis.

If two lines have the same slope, then they are **parallel**. Likewise, if two lines are parallel, then they have the same slope. That is, parallel lines have the same slope.

Two lines are **perpendicular** if the product of their lopes is -1. The slopes of perpendicular lines are the negative reciprocals of each other, that is, m and $-\frac{1}{m}$.

Note that $m \cdot \left(\frac{-1}{m}\right) = -1$.

Examples: 3 and $-\frac{1}{3}$, $-\frac{2}{3}$ and $\frac{3}{2}$, $\frac{5}{4}$ and $-\frac{4}{5}$

Two distinct lines on a flat surface that are not parallel intersect in a single point.

Example 1

Graph the linear equation $y = \frac{4}{7}x + 2$.

Using $y = mx + b$, the slope in $y = \frac{4}{7}x + 2$ is $\frac{4}{7}$ and the y-intercept is the point $(0, 2)$. To graph the line, begin at the y-intercept, $(0, 2)$. Remember that slope is $\frac{\text{vertical change}}{\text{horizontal change}}$ so go up 4 units (since 4 is positive) from $(0, 2)$ and then move right 7 units. This gives a second point on the graph, $(7, 6)$. To create the graph, draw a straight line through the two points.

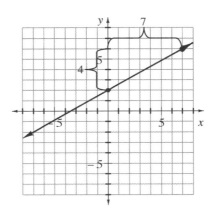

Example 2

A line has a slope of $\frac{3}{4}$ and passes through the point $(3, 2)$. What is the equation of the line?

Using $y = mx + b$, write $y = \frac{3}{4}x + b$. Since $(3, 2)$ represents a point (x, y) on the line, substitute 3 for x and 2 for y, then solve for b. This is shown in the work at right. Since $b = -\frac{1}{4}$, the equation is $y = \frac{3}{4}x - \frac{1}{4}$.

$$(2) = \frac{3}{4}(3) + b$$
$$2 = \frac{9}{4} + b$$
$$2 - \frac{9}{4} = b$$
$$b = -\frac{1}{4}$$

Example 3

Decide if the two lines at right are parallel, perpendicular, or neither (i.e., intersecting).

$5x - 4y = -6$ and $-4x + 5y = 3$

First find the slope of each equation. Then compare the slopes.

$$5x - 4y = -6$$
$$-4y = -5x - 6$$
$$y = \frac{-5x - 6}{-4}$$
$$y = \frac{5}{4}x + \frac{3}{2}$$

The slope of this line is $\frac{5}{4}$.

$$-4x + 5y = 3$$
$$5y = 4x + 3$$
$$y = \frac{4x + 3}{5}$$
$$y = \frac{4}{5}x + \frac{3}{5}$$

The slope of this line is $\frac{4}{5}$.

These two slopes are not equal, so they are not parallel. They intersect. The product of the two slopes is 1, not −1, so they are not perpendicular.

Example 4

Write the equations of the lines through the given point, one parallel and one perpendicular to the given line $y = -\frac{5}{2}x + 5$ and point $(-4, 5)$.

For the parallel line, use $y = mx + b$ with the same slope to write $y = -\frac{5}{2}x + b$.

Substitute the point $(-4, 5)$ for x and y and solve for b.

$$5 = -\frac{5}{2}(-4) + b$$
$$5 = \frac{20}{2} + b$$
$$b = -5$$

Therefore the equation of the parallel line through $(-4, 5)$ is $y = -\frac{5}{2}x - 5$.

For the perpendicular line, use $y = mx + b$ where m is the negative reciprocal of the slope of the original equation to write $y = \frac{2}{5}x + b$.

Substitute the point $(-4, 5)$ and solve for b.

$$5 = \frac{2}{5}(-4) + b$$
$$5 = -\frac{8}{5} + b$$

Therefore the equation of the perpendicular line through $(-4, 5)$ is $y = \frac{2}{5}x + \frac{33}{5}$. $b = \frac{33}{5}$

Problems

Identify the *y*-intercept in each equation.

1. $y = \frac{1}{2}x - 2$

2. $y = -\frac{3}{5}x - \frac{5}{3}$

3. $3x + 2y = 12$

4. $x - y = -13$

5. $2x - 4y = 12$

6. $4y - 2x = 12$

Write the equation of the line with:

7. A slope = $\frac{1}{2}$ and passing through the point $(4, 3)$.

8. A slope = $\frac{2}{3}$ and passing through the point $(-3, -2)$.

9. A slope = $-\frac{1}{3}$ and passing through the point $(4, -1)$.

10. A slope = -4 and passing through the point $(-3, 5)$.

Determine the slope of each line using the highlighted points.

11.

12.

13.

Using the slope and *y*-intercept, determine the equation of the line.

14.

15.

16.

17.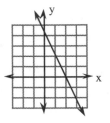

Graph the following linear equations on graph paper.

18. $y = \frac{1}{2}x + 3$

19. $y = -\frac{3}{5}x - 1$

20. $y = 4x$

21. $y = -6x + \frac{1}{2}$

22. $3x + 2y = 12$

State whether each pair of lines is parallel, perpendicular, or neither.

23. $y = 2x - 2$ and $y = 2x + 4$

24. $y = \frac{1}{2}x + 3$ and $y = -2x - 4$

25. $x - y = 2$ and $x + y = 3$

26. $y - x = -1$ and $y + x = 3$

27. $x + 3y = 6$ and $y = -\frac{1}{3}x - 3$

28. $3x + 2y = 6$ and $2x + 3y = 6$

29. $4x = 5y - 3$ and $4y = 5x + 3$

30. $3x - 4y = 12$ and $4y = 3x + 7$

Write an equation for the line through the given point and parallel to the given line.

31. $y = 2x - 2$ and $(-3, 5)$

32. $y = \frac{1}{2}x + 3$ and $(-4, 2)$

33. $x - y = 2$ and $(-2, 3)$

34. $y - x = -1$ and $(-2, 1)$

35. $x + 3y = 6$ and $(-1, 1)$

36. $3x + 2y = 6$ and $(2, -1)$

37. $4x = 5y - 3$ and $(1, -1)$

38. $3x - 4y = 12$ and $(4, -2)$

Write an equation for the line through the given point and perpendicular to the given line.

39. $y = 2x - 2$ and $(-3, 5)$

40. $y = \frac{1}{2}x + 3$ and $(-4, 2)$

41. $x - y = 2$ and $(-2, 3)$

42. $y - x = -1$ and $(-2, 1)$

43. $x + 3y = 6$ and $(-1, 1)$

44. $3x + 2y = 6$ and $(2, -1)$

45. $4x = 5y - 3$ and $(1, -1)$

46. $3x - 4y = 12$ and $(4, -2)$

Write an equation for the line parallel to each line below through the given point.

47.

48.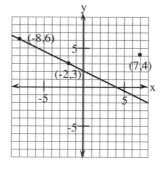

49. Write the equation of the line passing through the point $(7, -8)$ which is parallel to the line through the points $(2, 5)$ and $(8, -3)$.

50. Write the equation of the line passing through the point $(1, -4)$ which is parallel to the line through the points $(-3, -7)$ and $(4, 3)$.

Answers

1. $(0, -2)$

2. $(0, -\frac{5}{3})$

3. $(0, 6)$

4. $(0, 13)$

5. $(0, -3)$

6. $(0, 6)$

7. $y = \frac{1}{2}x + 1$

8. $y = \frac{2}{3}x$

9. $y = -\frac{1}{3}x + \frac{1}{3}$

10. $y = -4x - 7$

11. $-\frac{1}{2}$

12. $\frac{3}{4}$

13. -2

14. $y = 2x - 2$

15. $y = -x + 2$

16. $y = \frac{1}{3}x + 2$

17. $y = -2x + 4$

18. slope = $\frac{1}{2}$,
    y-intercept $(0, 3)$

19. slope = $-\frac{3}{5}$,
    y-intercept $(0, -1)$

20. slope = 4,
    y-intercept $(0, 0)$

21. slope = -6,
    y-intercept $(0, \frac{1}{2})$

22. slope $-\frac{3}{2}$,
    y-intercept $(0, 6)$

23. parallel

24. perpendicular

25. perpendicular

26. perpendicular

27. parallel

28. intersecting

29. intersecting

30. parallel

31. $y = 2x + 11$

32. $y = \frac{1}{2}x + 4$

33. $y = x + 5$

34. $y = x + 3$

35. $y = \frac{1}{3}x + \frac{2}{3}$

36. $y = -\frac{3}{2}x + 2$

37. $y = \frac{4}{5}x - \frac{9}{5}$

38. $y = \frac{3}{4}x - 5$

39. $y = -\frac{1}{2}x + \frac{7}{2}$

40. $y = -2x - 6$

41. $y = -x + 1$

42. $y = -x - 1$

43. $y = 3x + 4$

44. $y = \frac{2}{3}x - \frac{7}{3}$

45. $y = -\frac{5}{4}x + \frac{1}{4}$

46. $y = -\frac{4}{3}x + \frac{10}{3}$

47. $y = 3x + 11$

48. $y = -\frac{1}{2}x + \frac{15}{2}$

49. $y = -\frac{4}{3}x + \frac{4}{3}$

50. $y = \frac{10}{7}x - \frac{38}{7}$

SOLVING LINEAR SYSTEMS

You can find where two lines intersect (cross) by using algebraic methods. The two most common methods are the **Substitution** and **Elimination** (also known as the addition) **Methods**.

Example 1

Solve the following system of equations at right by using the Substitution Method. Check your solution.

$$y = 5x + 1$$
$$y = -3x - 15$$

When solving a system of equations, you are solving to find the x- and y-values that result in true statements when you substitute them into *both* equations. Since both equations are in y-form (that is, solved for y), and we know $y = y$, we can substitute the right side of each equation for y in the simple equation $y = y$ and write $5x + 1 = -3x - 15$. Then solve for x as shown at right.

$$5x + 1 = -3x - 15$$
$$8x + 1 = -15$$
$$8x = -16$$
$$x = -2$$

Remember you must find x *and* y. To find y, use either of the two original equations. Substitute the value of x into the equation and find the value of y.

$$y = 5x + 1$$
$$y = 5(-2) + 1$$
$$y = -9$$

The solution appears to be $(-2, -9)$. In order for this to be a solution, it must make both equations true when you replace x with -2 and y with -9. Substitute the values in both equations to check.

$$y = 5x + 1$$
$$-9 \overset{?}{=} 5(-2) + 1$$
$$-9 \overset{?}{=} -10 + 1$$
$$-9 = -9 \text{ Check!}$$

$$y = -3x - 15$$
$$-9 \overset{?}{=} -3(-2) - 15$$
$$-9 \overset{?}{=} 6 - 15$$
$$-9 = -9 \text{ Check!}$$

Therefore, $(-2, -9)$ is the solution.

Example 2

Substitution can also be used when the equations are *not* in y-form. Solve the system of equations at right by using the Substitution Method. Check your solution.

$$x = -3y + 1$$
$$4x - 3y = -11$$

Rewrite the two equations as $4(-3y + 1) - 3y = -11$ by replacing x with $(-3y + 1)$, then solve for y as shown at right below.

Substitute $y = 1$ into $x = -3y + 1$. Solve for x, and write the answer for x and y as an ordered pair, $(1, -2)$. Substitute $y = 1$ into $4x - 3y = -11$ to verify that either original equation may be used to find the second coordinate. Check your answer as shown in Example 1.

$$x = \overbrace{-3y + 1}$$
$$4(\ \nearrow\ ) - 3y = -11$$
$$4(-3y + 1) - 3y = -11$$
$$y = 1$$

Example 3

When you have a pair of two-variable equations, sometimes it is easier to **eliminate** one of the variables to obtain one single variable equation. You can do this by adding the two equations together as shown in the example below.

Solve the system at right.
$$2x + y = 11$$
$$x - y = 4$$

To eliminate the y-terms, add the two equations together then solve for x.

$$\begin{array}{r} 2x + y = 11 \\ + \quad x - y = 4 \\ \hline 3x = 15 \\ x = 5 \end{array}$$

Once we know the x-value we can substitute it into either of the original equations to find the corresponding value of y. The first equation is shown at right.

$$2x + y = 11$$
$$2(5) + y = 11$$
$$10 + y = 11$$
$$y = 1$$

Check the solution by substituting both the x-value and y-value into the other original equation.

$$x - y = 4$$
$$5 - 1 = 4$$
$$4 = 4 \quad \text{Check!}$$

Example 4

You can solve the system of equations at right by using the Elimination Method, but before you can eliminate one of the variables, you must adjust the coefficients of one of the variables so that they are additive opposites.

$$3x + 2y = 11$$
$$4x + 3y = 14$$

To eliminate y, multiply the first equation by 3, then multiply the second equation by –2 to get the equations at right.

$$9x + 6y = 33$$
$$-8x - 6y = -28$$

Next eliminate the y-terms by adding the two new equations.

Since $x = 5$, substitute 5 for x in either original equation to find that $y = -2$. The solution to the system of equations is $(5, -2)$.

$$\begin{array}{r} 9x + 6y = 33 \\ + \quad -8x - 6y = -28 \\ \hline x = 5 \end{array}$$

You could also solve the system by multiplying the first equation by 4 and the second equation by –3 to eliminate x, then proceed as shown above to find y.

Problems

Solve the following systems of equations to find the point of intersection (x, y) for each pair of lines.

1. $y = x - 6$
   $y = 12 - x$

2. $y = 3x - 5$
   $y = x + 3$

3. $x = 7 + 3y$
   $x = 4y + 5$

4. $x = -3y + 10$
   $x = -6y - 2$

5. $y = x + 7$
   $y = 4x - 5$

6. $y = 7 - 3x$
   $y = 2x - 8$

7. $y = 3x - 1$
   $2x - 3y = 10$

8. $x = -\frac{1}{2}y + 4$
   $8x + 3y = 31$

9. $2y = 4x + 10$
   $6x + 2y = 10$

10. $y = \frac{3}{5}x - 2$
    $y = \frac{x}{10}y + 1$

11. $y = 4x + 5$
    $y = x$

12. $4x - 3y = -10$
    $x = \frac{1}{4}y - 1$

13. $x + y = 12$
    $x - y = 4$

14. $2x - y = 6$
    $4x - y = 12$

15. $x + 2y = 7$
    $5x - 4y = 14$

16. $5x - 2y = 6$
    $4x + y = 10$

17. $x + y = 10$
    $x - 2y = 5$

18. $3y - 2x = 16$
    $y = 2x + 4$

19. $x + y = 11$
    $x = y - 3$

20. $x + 2y = 15$
    $y = x - 3$

21. $y + 5x = 10$
    $y - 3x = 14$

22. $y = 7x - 3$
    $4x + 2y = 8$

23. $y = 12 - x$
    $y = x - 4$

24. $y = 6 - 2x$
    $y = 4x - 12$

Answers

1. $(9, 3)$

2. $(4, 7)$

3. $(13, 2)$

4. $(22, -4)$

5. $(4, 11)$

6. $(3, -2)$

7. $(-1, -4)$

8. $(\frac{7}{2}, 1)$

9. $(0, 5)$

10. $(6, 1.6)$

11. $(1, 1)$

12. $(-0.25, 3)$

13. $(8, 4)$

14. $(3, 0)$

15. $(4, 1.5)$

16. $(2, 2)$

17. $(\frac{25}{3}, \frac{5}{3})$

18. $(1, 6)$

19. $(4, 7)$

20. $(7, 4)$

21. $(-0.5, 12.5)$

22. $(\frac{7}{9}, \frac{22}{9})$

23. $(8, 4)$

24. $(3, 0)$

To graph a linear inequality, first graph the line for the corresponding equality. This line is known as the boundary line, since all the points that make the inequality true lie on one side or the other of the line. Before you draw the boundary line, decide whether the it is part of the solution or not, that is, whether the line is solid or dashed. If the inequality symbol is either ≤ or ≥, then the boundary line is part of the inequality and it must be solid. If the symbol is either < or >, then the boundary line is not part of the inequality and it must be dashed.

Next, decide which side of the boundary line must be shaded to show the coordinates (points) on the graph that that make the inequality true. To do this, choose a point not on the line. Substitute this point into the *original* inequality. If the inequality is true for this point, then shade the graph on this side of the line. If the inequality is false for the point, then shade the graph on the *opposite* side of the line.

Note: If the inequality is not in Slope-Intercept form and you have to solve it for *y*, *always* use the *original* inequality to test a point, *not* the *y*-form form.

Example 1

Graph the inequality $y > 3x - 2$.

First, graph the line $y = 3x - 2$, but draw it dashed since > means the boundary line is not part of the solution.

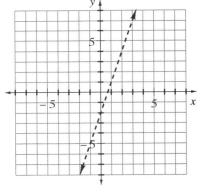

Next, test the point $(-2, 4)$ to the left of the boundary line.

$$4 > 3(-2) - 2, \text{ so } 4 > -8$$

Since the inequality is *true* for this point, shade the graph on the left side of the boundary line.

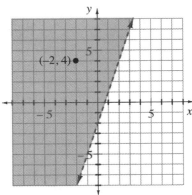

Example 2

Graph the system of inequalities
$y \le \frac{1}{2}x + 2$ and $y > -\frac{2}{3}x - 1$. ·

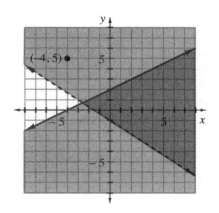

Graph the lines $y = -\frac{3}{5}x + 4$
and $y = -\frac{2}{3}x - 1$. The first line
is solid, the second is dashed.

Test the point (–4, 5) in the first inequality.

This inequality is false, so shade on the opposite side of the
boundary line, from (–4, 5).

$5 \overset{?}{\le} \frac{1}{2}(-4) + 2$, so $5 \le 0$

Test the same point in the second inequality.

This inequality is true, so shade on the same side of the
boundary line as (–4, 5).

$5 \overset{?}{>} -\frac{2}{3}(-4) - 1$, so $5 > \frac{5}{3}$

The solution is the overlap of the two shaded regions shown by the darkest shading in the second
graph above right.

Problems

Graph each of the following inequalities on separate sets of axes.

1. $y \le 3x + 1$ 2. $y \ge 2x - 1$ 3. $y \ge -2x - 3$ 4. $y \le -3x + 4$

5. $y > 4x + 2$ 6. $y < 2x + 1$ 7. $y < -3x - 5$ 8. $y > -5x - 4$

9. $y \le 3$ 10. $y \ge -2$ 11. $x > 1$ 12. $x \le 8$

13. $y > \frac{2}{3}x + 8$ 14. $y \le -\frac{2}{3}x + 3$ 15. $y \le -\frac{3}{7}x - 7$ 16. $y \ge \frac{1}{4}x - 2$

17. $3x + 2y \ge 7$ 18. $2x - 3y \le 5$ 19. $-4x + 2y < 3$ 20. $-3x - 4y > 4$

Graph each of the following pairs of inequalities on the same set of axes.

21. $y > 3x - 4$ and $y \le -2x + 5$ 22. $y \ge -3x - 6$ and $y > 4x - 4$

23. $y \le -\frac{3}{5}x + 4$ and $y \le \frac{1}{3}x + 3$ 24. $y < -\frac{3}{7}x - 1$ and $y > \frac{4}{5}x + 1$

25. $y < 3$ and $y \le -\frac{1}{2}x + 2$ 26. $x \le 3$ and $y < \frac{3}{4}x - 4$

Write an inequality for each of the following graphs.

27.

28.

29.

30.

31.

32.

Answers

1.

2.

3.

4.

5.

6.

7.

8.

9.

10.

11.

12.

13.

14.

15.

16.

17.

18.

19.

20.

21.

22.

23.

24.

25.

26.

27. $y \le x + 5$

28. $y \ge -\frac{5}{2}x + 5$

29. $y \le \frac{1}{5}x + 4$

30. $y > -4x + 1$

31. $x \ge -4$

32. $y \le 3$

MULTIPLYING POLYNOMIALS

We can use generic rectangles as area models to find the products of polynomials. A generic rectangle helps us organize the problem. It does not have to be drawn accurately or to scale.

Example 1

Multiply $(2x + 5)(x + 3)$

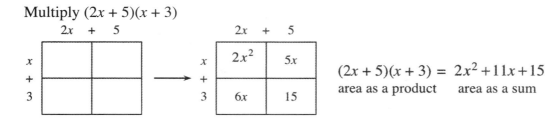

$(2x + 5)(x + 3) = 2x^2 + 11x + 15$
area as a product   area as a sum

Example 2

Multiply $(x + 9)(x^2 - 3x + 5)$

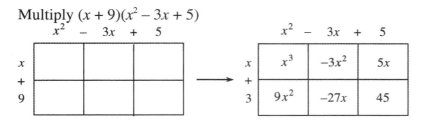

Therefore $(x + 9)(x^2 - 3x + 5) = x^3 + 9x^2 - 3x^2 - 27x + 5x + 45 = x^3 + 6x^2 - 22x + 45$

Example 3

The Distributive Property can be used for multiplying binominals without the area model. Multiplying each term of the first binomial by each term of the second binomial and then finding the sum. To remember the four steps some use the mnemonic "F.O.I.L." F.O.I.L. is an acronym for First, Outside, Inside, Last in reference to the positions of the terms in the two binomials.

Multiply $(3x - 2)(4x + 5)$ using the F.O.I.L. method.

F.	multiply the FIRST terms of each binomial	$(3x)(4x) = 12x^2$
O.	multiply the OUTSIDE terms	$(3x)(5) = 15x$
I.	multiply the INSIDE terms	$(-2)(4x) = -8x$
L.	multiply the LAST terms of each binomial	$(-2)(5) = -10$

Finally, we combine like terms: $12x^2 + 15x - 8x - 10 = 12x^2 + 7x - 10$

Problems

Find each of the following products.

1. $(3x + 2)(2x + 7)$
2. $(4x + 5)(5x + 3)$
3. $(2x - 1)(3x + 1)$

4. $(2a - 1)(4a + 7)$
5. $(m - 5)(m + 5)$
6. $(y - 4)(y + 4)$

7. $(3x - 1)(x + 2)$
8. $(3a - 2)(a - 1)$
9. $(2y - 5)(y + 4)$

10. $(3t - 1)(3t + 1)$
11. $(3y - 5)^2$
12. $(4x - 1)^2$

13. $(2x + 3)^2$
14. $(5n + 1)^2$
15. $(3x - 1)(2x^2 + 4x + 3)$

16. $(2x + 7)(4x^2 - 3x + 2)$
17. $(x + 7)(3x^2 - x + 5)$
18. $(x - 5)(x^2 - 7x + 1)$

19. $(3x + 2)(x^3 - 7x^2 + 3x)$
20. $(2x + 3)(3x^2 + 2x - 5)$

Answers

1. $6x^2 + 25x + 14$
2. $20x^2 + 37x + 15$
3. $6x^2 - x - 1$

4. $8a^2 + 10a - 7$
5. $m^2 - 25$
6. $y^2 - 16$

7. $3x^2 + 5x - 2$
8. $3a^2 - 5a + 2$
9. $2y^2 + 3y - 20$

10. $9t^2 - 1$
11. $9y^2 - 30y + 25$
12. $16x^2 - 8x + 1$

13. $4x^2 + 12x + 9$
14. $25n^2 + 10n + 1$
15. $6x^3 + 10x^2 + 5x - 3$

16. $8x^3 + 22x^2 - 17x + 14$
17. $3x^3 + 20x^2 - 2x + 35$
18. $x^3 - 12x^2 + 36x - 5$

19. $3x^4 - 19x^3 - 5x^2 + 6x$
20. $6x^3 + 13x^2 - 4x - 1$

Often we want to un-multiply or **factor** a polynomial $P(x)$. This process involves finding a constant and/or another polynomial that evenly divides the given polynomial. In formal mathematical terms, this means $P(x) = q(x) \cdot r(x)$, where q and r are also polynomials. In elementary algebra there are three general types of factoring.

1. **Common term** (finding the largest common factor):
   $6x + 18 = 6(x + 3)$ where 6 is a common factor of both terms.
   $2x^3 - 8x^2 - 10x = 2x(x^2 - 4x - 5)$ where $2x$ is the common factor.
   $2x^2(x - 1) + 7(x - 1) = (x - 1)(2x^2 + 7)$ where $x - 1$ is the common factor.

2. **Special products**
   $a^2 - b^2 = (a + b)(a - b)$ 　　　$x^2 - 25 = (x + 5)(x - 5)$
   　　　　　　　　　　　　　　　　$9x^2 - 4y^2 = (3x + 2y)(3x - 2y)$
   $x^2 + 2xy + y^2 = (x + y)^2$ 　　$x^2 + 8x + 16 = (x + 4)^2$
   $x^2 - 2xy + y^2 = (x - y)^2$ 　　$x^2 - 8x + 16 = (x - 4)^2$

3a. **Trinomials** in the form $x^2 + bx + c$ where the coefficient of x^2 is 1.
   Consider $x^2 + (d + e)\, x + d \cdot e = (x + d)(x + e)$, where the coefficient of x is the *sum* of two numbers d and e and the constant term is the *product* of the same two numbers, d and e. A quick way to determine all of the possible pairs of integers d and e is to factor the constant in the original trinomial. For example, 12 is $1 \cdot 12$, $2 \cdot 6$, and $3 \cdot 4$. The signs of the two numbers are determined by the combination you need to get the sum. The "sum and product" approach to factoring trinomials is the same as solving a "Diamond Problem" (see below).

   $x^2 + 8x + 15 = (x + 3)(x + 5);\ \ 3 + 5 = 8,\ 3 \cdot 5 = 15$
   $x^2 - 2x - 15 = (x - 5)(x + 3);\ \ -5 + 3 = -2,\ -5 \cdot 3 = -15$
   $x^2 - 7x + 12 = (x - 3)(x - 4);\ \ -3 + (-4) = -7,\ (-3)(-4) = 12$

   The sum and product approach can be shown visually using rectangles for an area model. The figure at far left below shows the "Diamond Problem" format for finding a sum and product. Here is how to use this method to factor $x^2 + 6x + 8$.

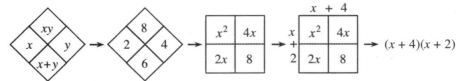

   Explanation and examples continue on the next page →

Explanation and examples continued from previous page.

3b. **Trinomials** in the form $ax^2 + bx + c$ where $a \neq 1$.

Note that the upper value in the diamond is no longer the constant. Rather, it is the *product* of a and c, that is, the coefficient of x^2 and the constant.

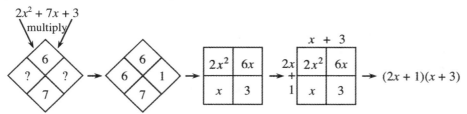

Below is the process to factor $5x^2 - 13x + 6$.

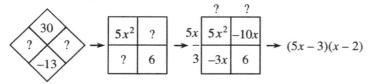

Polynomials with four or more terms are generally factored by grouping the terms and using one or more of the three procedures shown above. Note that polynomials are usually factored *completely*. In the second example in part (1) above, the trinomial also needs to be factored. Thus, the complete factorization of
$2x^3 - 8x^2 - 10x = 2x(x^2 - 4x - 5) = 2x(x - 5)(x + 1)$.

Problems

Factor each polynomial completely.

1. $x^2 - x - 42$

2. $4x^2 - 18$

3. $2x^2 + 9x + 9$

4. $2x^2 + 3xy + y^2$

5. $6x^2 - x - 15$

6. $4x^2 - 25$

7. $x^2 - 28x + 196$

8. $7x^2 - 847$

9. $x^2 + 18x + 81$

10. $x^2 + 4x - 21$

11. $3x^2 + 21x$

12. $3x^2 - 20x - 32$

13. $9x^2 - 16$

14. $4x^2 + 20x + 25$

15. $x^2 - 5x + 6$

16. $5x^3 + 15x^2 - 20x$

17. $4x^2 + 18$

18. $x^2 - 12x + 36$

19. $x^2 - 3x - 54$

20. $6x^2 - 21$

21. $2x^2 + 15x + 18$

22. $16x^2 - 1$

23. $x^2 - 14x + 49$

24. $x^2 + 8x + 15$

25. $3x^3 - 12x^2 - 45x$

26. $3x^2 + 24$

27. $x^2 + 16x - 64$

Factor completely.

28. $75x^3 - 27x$ 29. $3x^3 - 12x^2 - 36x$ 30. $4x^3 - 44x^2 + 112x$

31. $5y^2 - 125$ 32. $3x^2y^2 - xy^2 - 4y^2$ 33. $x^3 + 10x^2 - 24x$

34. $3x^3 - 6x^2 - 45x$ 35. $3x^2 - 27$ 36. $x^4 - 16$

Factor each of the following completely. Use the modified diamond approach.

37. $2x^2 + 5x - 7$ 38. $3x^2 - 13x + 4$ 39. $2x^2 + 9x + 10$

40. $4x^2 - 13x + 3$ 41. $4x^2 + 12x + 5$ 42. $6x^3 + 31x^2 + 5x$

43. $64x^2 + 16x + 1$ 44. $7x^2 - 33x - 10$ 45. $5x^2 + 12x - 9$

Answers

1. $(x + 6)(x - 7)$ 2. $2(2x^2 - 9)$ 3. $(2x + 3)(x + 3)$

4. $(2x + y)(x + y)$ 5. $(2x + 3)(3x - 5)$ 6. $(2x - 5)(2x + 5)$

7. $(x - 14)^2$ 8. $7(x - 11)(x + 11)$ 9. $(x + 9)^2$

10. $(x + 7)(x - 3)$ 11. $3x(x + 7)$ 12. $(x - 8)(3x + 4)$

13. $(3x - 4)(3x + 4)$ 14. $(2x + 5)^2$ 15. $(x - 3)(x - 2)$

16. $5x(x + 4)(x - 1)$ 17. $2(2x^2 + 9)$ 18. $(x - 6)^2$

19. $(x - 9)(x + 6)$ 20. $3(2x^2 - 7)$ 21. $(2x + 3)(x + 6)$

22. $(4x + 1)(4x - 1)$ 23. $(x - 7)^2$ 24. $(x + 3)(x + 5)$

25. $3x(x^2 - 4x - 15)$ 26. $3(x^2 + 8)$ 27. $(x + 8)^2$

28. $3x(5x - 3)(5x + 3)$ 29. $3x(x - 6)(x + 2)$ 30. $4x(x - 7)(x - 4)$

31. $5(y + 5)(y - 5)$ 32. $y^2(3x - 4)(x + 1)$ 33. $x(x + 12)(x - 2)$

34. $3x(x - 5)(x + 3)$ 35. $3(x - 3)(x + 3)$ 36. $(x - 2)(x + 2)(x^2 + 4)$

37. $(2x + 7)(x - 1)$ 38. $(3x - 1)(x - 4)$ 39. $(x + 2)(2x + 5)$

40. $(4x - 1)(x - 3)$ 41. $(2x + 5)(2x + 1)$ 42. $x(6x + 1)(x + 5)$

43. $(8x + 1)^2$ 44. $(7x + 2)(x - 5)$ 45. $(5x - 3)(x + 3)$

GRAPHING QUADRATICS AND THE ZERO PRODUCT PROPERTY

If $a \cdot b = 0$, then either $a = 0$ or $b = 0$.

Note that this property states that *at least* one of the factors *must* be zero. This simple statement gives us a powerful result which is most often used with equations involving the products of binomials. For example, solve $(x + 5)(x - 2) = 0$.

By the Zero Product Property, since $(x + 5)(x - 2) = 0$, either $x + 5 = 0$ or $x - 2 = 0$. Thus, $x = -5$ or $x = 2$.

The Zero Product Property can be used to find where a quadratic function crosses the x-axis. These points are the x-intercepts. Using the example above, if $y = (x + 5)(x - 2)$, the x-intercepts would be $(-5, 0)$ and $(2, 0)$.

Example 1

Where does $y = (x + 3)(x - 7)$ cross the x-axis?

Since $y = 0$ at the x-axis, then $(x + 3)(x - 7) = 0$ and the Zero Product Property tells you that $x = -3$ or $x = 7$ so $y = (x + 3)(x - 7)$ crosses the x-axis at $(-3, 0)$ and $(7, 0)$.

Example 2

Where does $y = x^2 - x - 6$ cross the x-axis?

First factor $x^2 - x - 6$ into $(x + 2)(x - 3)$ to get $y = (x + 2)(x - 3)$. By the Zero Product Property, the x-intercepts are $(-2, 0)$ and $(3, 0)$.

Example 3

Graph $y = x^2 - x - 6$.

Since you know the x-intercepts from Example 2, you already have two points to graph. Make a table of values to get additional points.

x	-2	-1	0	1	2	3	4
y	0	-4	-6	-6	-4	0	6

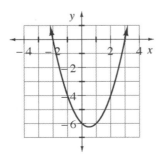

Example 4

Graph $y > x^2 - x - 6$.

First graph $y = x^2 - x - 6$. Use a dashed curve. Second, pick a point not on the parabola and substitute it into the inequality. For example, testing point $(0, 0)$ in $y > x^2 - x - 6$ gives $0 > -6$ which is a true statement. This means that $(0, 0)$ is a solution to the inequality as well as all points inside the curve. Shade the interior of the parabola.

Problems

Solve the following equations using the Zero Product Property.

1. $(x - 2)(x + 3) = 0$

2. $2x(x + 5)(x + 6) = 0$

3. $(x - 18)(x - 3) = 0$

4. $4x^2 - 5x - 6 = 0$

5. $(2x - 1)(x + 2) = 0$

6. $2x(x - 3)(x + 4) = 0$

7. $3x^2 - 13x - 10 = 0$

8. $2x^2 - x = 15$

Use factoring and the Zero Product Property to find the x-intercepts of each parabola below. Express your answer as ordered pair(s).

9. $y = x^2 - 3x + 2$

10. $y = x^2 - 10x + 25$

11. $y = x^2 - x - 12$

12. $y = x^2 - 4x - 5$

13. $y = x^2 + 2x - 8$

14. $y = x^2 + 6x + 9$

15. $y = x^2 - 8x + 16$

16. $y = x^2 - 9$

Graph the following inequalities. Be sure to use a test point to determine which region to shade. Your solutions to the previous problems might be helpful.

17. $y < x^2 - 3x + 2$

18. $y > x^2 - 10x + 25$

19. $y \le x^2 - x - 12$

20. $y \ge x^2 - 4x - 5$

21. $y > x^2 + 2x - 8$

22. $y \ge x^2 + 6x + 9$

23. $y < x^2 - 8x + 16$

24. $y \le x^2 - 9$

Answers

1. $x = 2, -3$

2. $x = 0, -5, -6$

3. $x = 18, 3$

4. $x = -0.75, 2$

5. $x = 0.5, -2$

6. $x = 0, 3, -4$

7. $x = -\frac{2}{3}, x = 5$

8. $x = -2.5, x = 3$

9. $(1, 0), (2, 0)$

10. $(5, 0)$

11. $(-3, 0), (4, 0)$

12. $(5, 0), (-1, 0)$

13. $(-4, 0), (2, 0)$

14. $(-3, 0)$

15. $(4, 0)$

16. $(3, 0), (-3, 0)$

17.

18.

19.

20.

21.

22.

23.

24.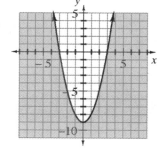

THE QUADRATIC FORMULA

You have used factoring and the Zero Product Property to solve quadratic equations. You can solve *any* quadratic equation by using the **Quadratic Formula**.

$$\text{If } ax^2 + bx + c = 0, \text{ then } x = \frac{-b \pm \sqrt{b^2 - 4ac}}{2a}.$$

For example, suppose $3x^2 + 7x - 6 = 0$. Here $a = 3$, $b = 7$, and $c = -6$.

Substituting these values into the formula results in:

$$x = \frac{-(7) \pm \sqrt{7^2 - 4(3)(-6)}}{2(3)} \Rightarrow x = \frac{-(7) \pm \sqrt{121}}{6} \Rightarrow x = \frac{-7 \pm 11}{6}$$

Remember that taking the square root of x^2 yields both a positive and a negative square root. The sign $\pm$ represents this fact for the square root in the formula and allows us to write the equation *once* (representing two possible solutions) until later in the solution process.

Split the numerator into the two values: $x = \frac{-7 + 11}{6}$ or $x = \frac{-7 - 11}{6}$

Thus the solution for the quadratic equation is: $x = \frac{2}{3}$ or -3

Example 1

Solve $x^2 + 3x - 2 = 0$ using the Quadratic Formula.

First, identify the values for a, b, and c. In this case they are $1, 3$, and -2, respectively. Next, substitute these values into the Quadratic Formula.

$$x = \frac{-(3) \pm \sqrt{3^2 - 4(1)(-2)}}{2(1)} \Rightarrow x = \frac{-3 \pm \sqrt{17}}{2}$$

Then split the numerator into the two values: $x = \frac{-3 + \sqrt{17}}{2}$ or $x = \frac{-3 - \sqrt{17}}{2}$

Using a calculator, the solution for the quadratic equation is: $x \approx 0.56$ or -3.56

Example 2

Solve $4x^2 + 4x = 3$ using the Quadratic Formula.

To solve any quadratic equation it must first be equal to zero. Rewrite the equation as $4x^2 + 4x - 3 = 0$. Identify the values for a, b, and c: $4, 4$, and -3, respectively.

Substitute these values into the Quadratic Formula: $x = \frac{-4 \pm \sqrt{4^2 - 4(4)(-3)}}{2(4)} \Rightarrow x = \frac{-4 \pm \sqrt{64}}{8} \Rightarrow x = \frac{-4 \pm 8}{8}$

Split the numerator into the two values: $x = \frac{-4+8}{8}$ or $x = \frac{-4-8}{8}$, so $x = \frac{1}{2}$ or $-\frac{3}{2}$.

Problems

Use the Quadratic Formula to solve each of the following equations.

1. $x^2 - x - 6 = 0$

2. $x^2 + 8x + 15 = 0$

3. $x^2 + 13x + 42 = 0$

4. $x^2 - 10x + 16 = 0$

5. $x^2 + 5x + 4 = 0$

6. $x^2 - 9x + 18 = 0$

7. $5x^2 - x - 4 = 0$

8. $4x^2 - 11x - 3 = 0$

9. $6x^2 - x - 15 = 0$

10. $6x^2 + 19x + 15 = 0$

11. $3x^2 + 5x - 28 = 0$

12. $2x^2 - x - 14 = 0$

13. $4x^2 - 9x + 4 = 0$

14. $2x^2 - 5x + 2 = 0$

15. $20x^2 + 20x = 1$

16. $13x^2 - 16x = 4$

17. $7x^2 + 28x = 0$

18. $5x^2 = -125x$

19. $8x^2 - 50 = 0$

20. $15x^2 = 3$

Answers

1. $x = -2, 3$

2. $x = -5, -3$

3. $x = -7, -6$

4. $x = 2, 8$

5. $x = -4, -1$

6. $x = 3, 6$

7. $x = -\frac{4}{5}, 1$

8. $x = -\frac{1}{4}, 3$

9. $x = -\frac{3}{2}, \frac{5}{3}$

10. $x = -\frac{3}{2}, -\frac{5}{3}$

11. $x = -4, \frac{7}{3}$

12. $x = \frac{1 \pm \sqrt{113}}{4}$

13. $x = \frac{9 \pm \sqrt{17}}{8}$

14. $x = 2, \frac{1}{2}$

15. $x = \frac{-20 \pm \sqrt{480}}{40}, = \frac{-5 \pm \sqrt{30}}{10}$

16. $x = \frac{16 \pm \sqrt{464}}{26}, = \frac{8 \pm 2\sqrt{29}}{13}$

17. $x = -4, 0$

18. $x = -25, 0$

19. $x = -\frac{5}{2}, \frac{5}{2}$

20. $x = \frac{\pm \sqrt{5}}{5}$

LAWS OF EXPONENTS

Here are the basic patterns with examples:

1. $x^a \cdot x^b = x^{a+b}$ Examples: $x^3 \cdot x^4 = x^{3+4} = x^7$; $2^7 \cdot 2^4 = 2^{11}$

2. $\dfrac{x^a}{x^b} = x^{a-b}$ Examples: $x^{10} \div x^4 = x^{10-4} = x^6$; $\dfrac{2^4}{2^7} = 2^{-3}$

3. $(x^a)^b = x^{ab}$ Examples: $(x^4)^3 = x^{4\cdot3} = x^{12}$; $(2x^3)^4 = 2^4 x^{12} = 16x^{12}$

4. $x^{-a} = \dfrac{1}{x^a}$ and $\dfrac{1}{x^{-b}} = x^b$ Examples: $3x^{-3}y^2 = \dfrac{3y^2}{x^3}$; $\dfrac{2x^5}{y^{-2}} = 2x^5 y^2$

5. $x^{a/b} = \sqrt[b]{x^a} = (\sqrt[b]{x})^a$ Examples: $x^{2/3} = \sqrt[3]{x^2}$; $8^{2/3} = \sqrt[3]{8^2} = \sqrt[3]{64} = 4$

Example 1

Rewrite in a simpler, equivalent form: $(2xy^3)(5x^2y^4)$

Multiply the coefficients: $2 \cdot 5 \cdot xy^3 \cdot x^2y^4 = 10xy^3 \cdot x^2y^4$

Add the exponents of x, then y: $10x^{1+2}y^{3+4} = 10x^3y^7$

Example 2

Rewrite in a simpler, equivalent form: $\dfrac{14x^2y^{12}}{7x^5y^7}$

Divide the coefficients: $\dfrac{(14 \div 7)x^2y^{12}}{x^5y^7} = \dfrac{2x^2y^{12}}{x^5y^7}$

Subtract the exponents: $2x^{2-5}y^{12-7} = 2x^{-3}y^5$ or $\dfrac{2y^5}{x^3}$

Example 3

Rewrite in a simpler, equivalent form: $(3x^2y^4)^3$

Cube each factor: $3^3 \cdot (x^2)^3 \cdot (y^4)^3 = 27(x^2)^3(y^4)^3$

Multiply the exponents: $27x^6y^{12}$

Example 4

Rewrite in a simpler, equivalent form: $(144x^{-12})^{1/2}$

Convert negative exponents and change to radical: $(144x^{-12})^{1/2} = (\frac{144}{x^{12}})^{1/2} = \sqrt{\frac{144}{x^{12}}} = \frac{12}{x^6}$

Problems

Rewrite each expression in a simpler, equivalent form.

1. $y^5 \cdot y^7$

2. $b^4 \cdot b^3 \cdot b^2$

3. $8^6 \cdot 8^2$

4. $(y^5)^2$

5. $(3a)^4$

6. $\dfrac{m^8}{m^3}$

7. $\dfrac{12x^9}{4x^4}$

8. $(x^3y^2)^3$

9. $\dfrac{(y^4)^2}{(y^3)^2}$

10. $\dfrac{15x^2y^7}{3x^4y^5}$

11. $(4c^4)(ac^3)(3a^5c)$

12. $(7x^3y^5)^2$

13. $(4xy^2)(2y)^3$

14. $\left(\dfrac{4}{x^2}\right)^3$

15. $\dfrac{(2a^7)(3a^2)}{6a^3}$

16. $\left(\dfrac{5m^3n}{m^5}\right)^3$

17. $(3a^2x^3)^2(2ax^4)^3$

18. $\left(\dfrac{x^3y}{y^4}\right)^4$

19. $\left(\dfrac{6y^2x^8}{12x^3y^7}\right)^2$

20. $\dfrac{(2x^5y^3)^3(4xy^4)^2}{8x^7y^{12}}$

21. $(-27)^{1/3}$

22. $16^{-1/2}$

23. $(16a^8b^{12})^{3/4}$

24. $\dfrac{144^{1/2}x^{-3}}{(16^{3/4}x^7)^0}$

Answers

1. y^{12}

2. b^9

3. 8^8

4. y^{10}

5. $81a^4$

6. m^5

7. $3x^5$

8. x^9y^6

9. y^2

10. $\dfrac{5y^2}{x^2}$

11. $12a^6c^8$

12. $49x^6y^{10}$

13. $32xy^5$

14. $\dfrac{64}{x^6}$

15. a^6

16. $\dfrac{125n^3}{m^6}$

17. $72a^7x^{18}$

18. $\dfrac{x^{12}}{y^{12}}$

19. $\dfrac{x^{10}}{4y^{10}}$

20. $16x^{10}y^5$

21. -3

22. $\dfrac{1}{4}$

23. $8a^6b^9$

24. $\dfrac{12}{3}$

Sometimes it is convenient to leave square roots in radical form instead of using a calculator to find approximations (decimal values). Look for perfect squares (i.e., $4, 9, 16, 25, 36, 49, ...$) as factors of the number that is inside the radical sign (**radicand**). Compute the square root(s) of any perfect square factor(s) and place the root(s) outside the radical to indicate the root multiplies the reduced radical. When there is already an existing value that multiplies the radical, multiply any root(s) by that value.

Examples:

$$\sqrt{9} = 3 \qquad\qquad\qquad 5\sqrt{9} = 5 \cdot 3 = 15$$

$$\sqrt{18} = \sqrt{9 \cdot 2} = \sqrt{9} \cdot \sqrt{2} = 3\sqrt{2} \qquad 3\sqrt{98} = 3\sqrt{49 \cdot 2} = 3 \cdot 7\sqrt{2} = 21\sqrt{2}$$

$$\sqrt{80} = \sqrt{16 \cdot 5} = \sqrt{16} \cdot \sqrt{5} = 4\sqrt{5} \qquad \sqrt{45} + 4\sqrt{20} = \sqrt{9 \cdot 5} + 4\sqrt{4 \cdot 5} = 3\sqrt{5} + 4 \cdot 2\sqrt{5} = 11\sqrt{5}$$

When there are no more perfect square factors inside the radical sign, the product of the whole number (or fraction) and the remaining radical is said to be in **simple radical form**.

Simple radical form does not allow radicals in the denominator of a fraction. If there is a radical in the denominator, **rationalize the denominator** by multiplying the numerator and denominator of the fraction by the radical in the original denominator. Then rewrite the remaining fraction.

Examples: $\frac{2}{\sqrt{2}} = \frac{2}{\sqrt{2}} \cdot \frac{\sqrt{2}}{\sqrt{2}} = \frac{2\sqrt{2}}{2} = \sqrt{2}$ $\qquad \frac{4\sqrt{5}}{\sqrt{6}} = \frac{4\sqrt{5}}{\sqrt{6}} \cdot \frac{\sqrt{6}}{\sqrt{6}} = \frac{4\sqrt{30}}{6} = \frac{2\sqrt{30}}{3}$

In the first example, $\sqrt{2} \cdot \sqrt{2} = \sqrt{4} = 2$ and $\frac{2}{2} = 1$.

In the second example, $\sqrt{6} \cdot \sqrt{6} = \sqrt{36} = 6$ and $\frac{4}{6} = \frac{2}{3}$.

Example 1

Add $\sqrt{27} + \sqrt{12} - \sqrt{48}$. Factor each radical and rewrite it in a simpler, equivalent form.

$$\sqrt{9 \cdot 3} + \sqrt{4 \cdot 3} - \sqrt{16 \cdot 3} = 3\sqrt{3} + 2\sqrt{3} - 4\sqrt{3} = 1\sqrt{3} \text{ or } \sqrt{3}$$

Example 2

Rewrite $\frac{3}{\sqrt{6}}$ in simple radical form.

Multiply by $\frac{\sqrt{6}}{\sqrt{6}}$ and reduce: $\frac{3}{\sqrt{6}} \cdot \frac{\sqrt{6}}{\sqrt{6}} = \frac{3\sqrt{6}}{6} = \frac{\sqrt{6}}{2}$.

Problems

Rewrite each of the following radicals in simple radical form.

1. $\sqrt{24}$

2. $\sqrt{48}$

3. $\sqrt{17}$

4. $\sqrt{31}$

5. $\sqrt{75}$

6. $\sqrt{50}$

7. $\sqrt{96}$

8. $\sqrt{243}$

9. $\sqrt{8} + \sqrt{18}$

10. $\sqrt{18} + \sqrt{32}$

11. $\sqrt{27} - \sqrt{12}$

12. $\sqrt{50} - \sqrt{32}$

13. $\sqrt{6} + \sqrt{63}$

14. $\sqrt{44} + \sqrt{99}$

15. $\sqrt{50} + \sqrt{32} - \sqrt{27}$

16. $\sqrt{75} - \sqrt{8} - \sqrt{32}$

17. $\frac{3}{\sqrt{3}}$

18. $\frac{5}{\sqrt{27}}$

19. $\frac{\sqrt{3}}{\sqrt{5}}$

20. $\frac{\sqrt{5}}{\sqrt{7}}$

21. $4\sqrt{5} - \frac{10}{\sqrt{5}}$

Answers

1. $2\sqrt{6}$

2. $4\sqrt{3}$

3. $\sqrt{17}$

4. $\sqrt{31}$

5. $5\sqrt{3}$

6. $5\sqrt{2}$

7. $4\sqrt{6}$

8. $9\sqrt{3}$

9. $5\sqrt{2}$

10. $7\sqrt{2}$

11. $\sqrt{3}$

12. $\sqrt{2}$

13. $3\sqrt{7} + \sqrt{6}$

14. $5\sqrt{11}$

15. $9\sqrt{2} - 3\sqrt{3}$

16. $5\sqrt{3} - 6\sqrt{2}$

17. $\sqrt{3}$

18. $\frac{5\sqrt{3}}{9}$

19. $\frac{\sqrt{15}}{5}$

20. $\frac{\sqrt{35}}{7}$

21. $2\sqrt{5}$

SOLVING BY REWRITING: FRACTION BUSTERS

Equations with fractions and/or decimals can be rewritten as equivalent equations without fractions and/or decimals and then solved in the usual manner. Equations can also be made simpler by factoring a common numerical factor out of each term. Fractions can be eliminated from an equation by multiplying *both* sides (i.e., all terms) of an equation by the common denominator. If you cannot easily determine the common denominator, then multiply the entire equation by the product of all of the denominators. We call the term used to eliminate the denominators a **fraction buster**. Always remember to check your solution(s).

Example 1

Solve: $0.12x + 7.5 = 0.2x + 3$

Multiply by 100 to remove the decimals.

$$100 \cdot (0.12x + 7.5 = 0.2x + 3)$$
$$12x + 750 = 20x + 300$$

Solve in the usual manner.

$$-8x = -450$$
$$x = 56.25$$

Example 2

Solve: $25x^2 + 125x + 150 = 0$

Divide by 25 (a common factor).

$$\frac{25x^2 + 125x + 150 = 0}{25}$$
$$x^2 + 5x + 6 = 0$$

Solve in the usual manner.

$$(x + 2)(x + 3) = 0$$
$$x = -2 \text{ or } x = -3$$

Example 3

Solve: $\frac{x}{2} + \frac{x}{6} = 7$

Multiply both sides of the equation by 6, the common denominator, to remove the fractions.

$$6 \cdot \left(\frac{x}{2} + \frac{x}{6} \right) = 6(7)$$

(Multiplying both sides by 12 would also have been acceptable.)

Distribute and solve as usual.

$$6 \cdot \frac{x}{2} + 6 \cdot \frac{x}{6} = 6 \cdot 7$$
$$3x + x = 42$$
$$4x = 42$$
$$x = \frac{42}{4} = \frac{21}{2} = 10.5$$

Example 4

Solve: $\frac{5}{2x} + \frac{1}{6} = 8$

Multiply both sides by $6x$, the common denominator, to remove the fractions.

$$6x \cdot \left(\frac{5}{2x} + \frac{1}{6} \right) = 6x(8)$$

(Multiplying both sides by $12x$ would also have been acceptable.)

Distribute and solve as usual.

$$6x \cdot \frac{5}{2x} + 6x \cdot \frac{1}{6} = 6x \cdot 8$$
$$15 + x = 48x$$
$$15 = 47x$$
$$x = \frac{15}{47} \approx 0.32$$

Problems

Rewrite each equation in a simpler form and then solve the new equation.

1. $\frac{x}{3} + \frac{x}{2} = 5$

2. $3000x + 2000 = -1000$

3. $0.02y - 1.5 = 17$

4. $\frac{x}{2} + \frac{x}{3} - \frac{x}{4} = 12$

5. $50x^2 - 200 = 0$

6. $\frac{x}{9} + \frac{2x}{5} = 3$

7. $\frac{3x}{10} + \frac{x}{10} = \frac{15}{10}$

8. $\frac{3}{2x} + \frac{5}{x} = \frac{13}{6}$

9. $x^2 - 2.5x + 1 = 0$

10. $\frac{2}{3x} - \frac{1}{x} = \frac{1}{36}$

11. $0.002x = 5$

12. $10 + \frac{5}{x} + \frac{3}{3x} = 11$

13. $0.3(x + 7) = 0.2(x - 2)$

14. $x + \frac{x}{2} + \frac{3x}{5} = 21$

15. $32 \cdot 3x - 32 \cdot 1 = 32 \cdot 8$

16. $5 + \frac{2}{x} + \frac{5}{4x} = \frac{73}{12}$

17. $\frac{17}{2x+1} = \frac{17}{5}$

18. $2 + \frac{6}{x} + \frac{6}{3x} = 3$

19. $2.5x^2 + 3x + 0.5 = 0$

20. $\frac{x}{x-2} = \frac{7}{x-2}$

Answers

1. $x = 6$

2. $x = -1$

3. $y = 925$

4. $x = \frac{144}{7} \approx 20.57$

5. $x = \pm 2$

6. $x = \frac{135}{23} \approx 5.87$

7. $x = \frac{15}{4} = 3.75$

8. $x = 3$

9. $x = \frac{1}{2}$ or 2

10. $x = -12$

11. $x = 2500$

12. $x = 6$

13. $x = -25$

14. $x = 10$

15. $x = 3$

16. $x = 3$

17. $x = 2$

18. $x = 8$

19. $x = -\frac{1}{5}$ or -1

20. $x = 7$ Note: x cannot be 2.

ARITHMETIC SEQUENCES

An ordered list of numbers such as: $4, 9, 16, 25, 36\ldots$ is a **sequence**. Each number in the sequence is a **term**. Usually variables with subscripts are used to label terms. For example, in the sequence above, the first term is 4 and the third term is 16. This might be written $a_1 = 4$ and $a_3 = 16$ where a is the variable used to label the sequence.

In the sequence $1, 5, 9, 13, \ldots$, there is a **common difference** ($d = 4$) between the successive terms and this is called an **arithmetic sequence**. There are two common methods to define a sequence. An explicit formula tells you exactly how to find any specific term in the sequence. A recursive formula tells first term and how to get from one term to the next. Formally, for arithmetic sequences, this is written:

Explicit: $a_n = a_1 + (n-1)d$ where n = term number and d = common difference.

Recursive: a_1 = some specific value, $a_{n+1} = a_n + d$, and d = common difference.

For the sequence $1, 5, 9, 13, \ldots$, the explicit formula is: $a_n = 1 + (n-1)(4) = 4n - 3$ and the recursive formula is: $a_1 = 1$, $a_{n+1} = a_n + 4$. In each case, successively replacing n by $1, 2, 3, \ldots$ will yield the terms of the sequence. See the examples below.

Example 1

List the first five terms of the arithmetic sequence.

$$a_n = 5n + 2 \quad \text{(an explicit formula)}$$

$a_1 = 5(1) + 2 = 7$
$a_2 = 5(2) + 2 = 12$
$a_3 = 5(3) + 2 = 17$
$a_4 = 5(4) + 2 = 22$
$a_5 = 5(5) + 2 = 27$

The sequence is: $7, 12, 17, 22, 27, \ldots$

Example 2

List the first five terms of the arithmetic sequence.

$$b_1 = 3$$
$$b_{n+1} = b_n - 5 \quad \text{(A recursive formula)}$$

$b_1 = 3$
$b_2 = b_1 - 5 = 3 - 5 = -2$
$b_3 = b_2 - 5 = -2 - 5 = -7$
$b_4 = b_3 - 5 = -7 - 5 = -12$
$b_5 = b_4 - 5 = -12 - 5 = -17$

The sequence is: $3, -2, -7, -12, -17, \ldots$

Example 3

Write an explicit and a recursive equation for the sequence: $-2, 1, 4, 7, \ldots$

Explicit: $a_1 = -2, d = 3$ so the equation is $a_n = a_1 + (n-1)d = -2 + (n-1)(3) = 3n - 5$

Recursive: $a_1 = -2, d = 3$ so the equation is $a_1 = -2$, $a_{n+1} = a_n + 3$.

Problems

List the first five terms of each arithmetic sequence.

1. $a_n = 5n - 2$
2. $b_n = -3n + 5$
3. $a_n = -15 + \frac{1}{2}n$
4. $c_n = 5 + 3(n - 1)$
5. $a_1 = 5,\ a_{n+1} = a_n + 3$
6. $a_1 = 5,\ a_{n+1} = a_n - 3$
7. $a_1 = -3,\ a_{n+1} = a_n + 6$
8. $a_1 = \frac{1}{3},\ a_{n+1} = a_n + \frac{1}{2}$

Find the 30th term of each arithmetic sequence.

9. $a_n = 5n - 2$
10. $a_n = -15 + \frac{1}{2}n$
11. $a_{31} = 53,\ d = 5$
12. $a_1 = 25,\ a_{n+1} = a_n - 3$

For each arithmetic sequence, find an explicit and a recursive formula.

13. $4, 8, 12, 16, 20, \ldots$
14. $-2, 5, 12, 19, 26, \ldots$
15. $27, 15, 3, -9, -21, \ldots$
16. $3, 3\frac{1}{3}, 3\frac{2}{3}, 4, 4\frac{1}{3}, \ldots$

Sequences are graphed using points of the form: (term number, term value). For example, the sequence $4, 9, 16, 25, 36, \ldots$ would be graphed by plotting the points $(1, 4), (2, 9), (3, 16)$, $(4, 25), (5, 36), \ldots$. Sequences are graphed as points and not connected.

17. Graph the sequences from problems 1 and 2 above and determine the slope of each line.

18. How do the slopes of the lines found in the previous problem relate to the sequences?

Answers

1. $3, 8, 13, 18, 23$
2. $2, -1, -4, -7, -10$

3. $-14\frac{1}{2}, -14, -13\frac{1}{2}, -13, -12\frac{1}{2}$
4. $5, 8, 11, 14, 17$

5. $5, 8, 11, 14, 17$ 6. $5, 2, -1, -4, -7$ 7. $-3, 3, 9, 15, 21$ 8. $\frac{1}{3}, \frac{5}{6}, 1\frac{1}{3}, 1\frac{5}{6}, 2\frac{1}{3}$

9. 148 10. 0 11. 48 12. -62

13. $a_n = 4n$; $a_1 = 4,\ a_{n+1} = a_n + 4$
14. $a_n = 7n - 9$; $a_1 = -2,\ a_{n+1} = a_n + 7$

15. $a_n = -12n + 39$; $a_1 = 27,\ a_{n+1} = a_n - 12$ 16. $a_n = \frac{1}{3}n + 2\frac{2}{3}$; $a_1 = 3,\ a_{n+1} = a_n + \frac{1}{3}$

17. Graph (1): $(1, 3), (2, 8), (3, 13), (4, 18), (5, 23)$; slope = 5
    Graph (2): $(1, 2), (2, -1), (3, -4), (4, -7), (5, -10)$; slope = -3

18. The slope of the line containing the points is the same as the common difference of the sequence.

GEOMETRIC SEQUENCES

In the sequence $2, 6, 18, 54, \ldots$, there is a common ratio ($r = 3$) between the successive terms and this is called an **geometric sequence**. There are two common methods to define a geometric sequence. The explicit formula tells you exactly how to find any specific term in the sequence. The recursive formula gives first term and how to get from one term to the next. Formally, for geometric sequences, this is written:

Explicit: $a_n = a_1 \cdot r^{n-1}$ where n = term number and r = common ratio.

Recursive: a_1 = some specific value and $a_{n+1} = a_n \cdot r$ where r = common ratio.

For the sequence $2, 6, 18, 54, \ldots$, the explicit formula is $a_n = a_1 \cdot r^{n-1} = 2 \cdot 3^{n-1}$, and the recursive formula is $a_1 = 2$, $a_{n+1} = a_n \cdot 3$. In each case, successively replacing n by $1, 2, 3, \ldots$ will yield the terms of the sequence. See the examples below.

Example 1

List the first five terms of the geometric sequence.

$$a_n = 3 \cdot 2^{n-1} \quad \text{(an explicit formula)}$$

$a_1 = 3 \cdot 2^{1-1} = 3 \cdot 2^0 = 3$
$a_2 = 3 \cdot 2^{2-1} = 3 \cdot 2^1 = 6$
$a_3 = 3 \cdot 2^{3-1} = 3 \cdot 2^2 = 12$
$a_4 = 3 \cdot 2^{4-1} = 3 \cdot 2^3 = 24$
$a_5 = 3 \cdot 2^{5-1} = 3 \cdot 2^4 = 48$

The sequence is: $3, 6, 12, 24, 48, \ldots$

Example 2

List the first five terms of the geometric sequence.

$$b_1 = 8$$
$$b_{n+1} = b_n \cdot \tfrac{1}{2} \quad \text{(a recursive formula)}$$

$b_1 = 8$
$b_2 = b_1 \cdot \frac{1}{2} = 8 \cdot \frac{1}{2} = 4$
$b_3 = b_2 \cdot \frac{1}{2} = 4 \cdot \frac{1}{2} = 2$
$b_4 = b_3 \cdot \frac{1}{2} = 2 \cdot \frac{1}{2} = 1$
$b_5 = b_4 \cdot \frac{1}{2} = 1 \cdot \frac{1}{2} = \frac{1}{2}$

The sequence is: $8, 4, 2, 1, \frac{1}{2}, \ldots$

Example 3

Write an explicit and a recursive equation for the sequence: $81, 27, 9, 3, \ldots$

Explicit: $a_1 = 81$, $r = \frac{1}{3}$ so the equation is $a_n = a_1 \cdot r^{n-1} = 81 \cdot \left(\frac{1}{3}\right)^{n-1}$.

Recursive: $a_1 = 81$, $r = \frac{1}{3}$ so the equation is $a_1 = 81$, $a_{n+1} = a_n \cdot \frac{1}{3}$.

Problems

List the first five terms of each geometric sequence.

1. $a_n = 5 \cdot 2^{n-1}$

2. $b_n = -3 \cdot 3^{n-1}$

3. $a_n = 40\left(\frac{1}{2}\right)^{n-1}$

4. $c_n = 6\left(-\frac{1}{2}\right)^{n-1}$

5. $a_1 = 5, \ a_{n+1} = a_n \cdot 3$

6. $a_1 = 100, \ a_{n+1} = a_n \cdot \frac{1}{2}$

7. $a_1 = -3, \ a_{n+1} = a_n \cdot (-2)$

8. $a_1 = \frac{1}{3}, \ a_{n+1} = a_n \cdot \frac{1}{2}$

Find the 15th term of each geometric sequence.

9. $b_{14} = 232, r = 2$

10. $b_{16} = 32, r = 2$

11. $a_{14} = 9, r = \frac{2}{3}$

12. $a_{16} = 9, r = \frac{2}{3}$

Find an explicit and a recursive formula for each geometric sequence.

13. $2, 10, 50, 250, 1250, \ldots$

14. $16, 4, 1, \frac{1}{4}, \frac{1}{16}, \ldots$

15. $5, 15, 45, 135, 405, \ldots$

16. $3, -6, 12, -24, 48, \ldots$

17. Graph the sequences from problems 1 and 14.

18. How are the graphs of geometric sequences different from arithmetic sequences?

Answers

1. $5, 10, 20, 40, 80$

2. $-3, -9, -27, -81, -243$

3. $40, 20, 10, 5, \frac{5}{2}$

4. $6, -3, \frac{3}{2}, -\frac{3}{4}, \frac{3}{8}$

5. $5, 15, 45, 135, 405$

6. $100, 50, 25, \frac{25}{2}, \frac{25}{4}$

7. $-3. 6, -12, 24, -48$

8. $\frac{1}{3}, \frac{1}{6}, \frac{1}{12}, \frac{1}{24}, \frac{1}{48}$

9. 464

10. 16

11. 6

12. $\frac{27}{2}$

13. $a_n = 2 \cdot 5^{n-1}$; $a_1 = 2, \ a_{n+1} = a_n \cdot 5$

14. $a_n = 16 \cdot \left(\frac{1}{4}\right)^{n-1}$; $a_1 = 16, \ a_{n+1} = a_n \cdot \frac{1}{4}$

15. $a_n = 5 \cdot 3^{n-1}$; $a_1 = 5, \ a_{n+1} = a_n \cdot 3$

16. $a_n = 3 \cdot (-2)^{n-1}$; $a_1 = 3, \ a_{n+1} = a_n \cdot (-2)$

17. Graph (1): $(1, 5), (2, 10), (3, 20), (4, 40), (5, 80)$
    Graph (14): $(1, 16), (2, 4), (3, 1), (4, \frac{1}{4}), (5, \frac{1}{16})$

18. Arithmetic sequences are linear and geometric sequences are curved (exponential).

EXPONENTIAL FUNCTIONS

> An exponential function has an equation of the form $y = ab^x$ (with $b \geq 0$).
>
> In many situations "a" represents a starting or initial value, "b" represents the multiplier or growth/decay factor, and "x" represents the time.

Example 1

Graph $y = 3 \cdot 2^x$.

Make a table of values.

x	−1	0	1	2	3
y	1.5	3	6	12	24

Plot the points and connect them to form a smooth curve.

$y = 3 \cdot 2^x$

This is called an **increasing** exponential curve.

Example 2

Graph $y = 2(0.75)^x$.

Make a table of values using a calculator.

x	−1	0	1	2	3
y	2.7	2	1.5	1.1	0.8

Plot the points and connect them to form a smooth curve.

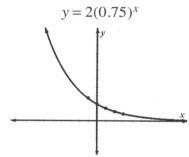

$y = 2(0.75)^x$

This is called a **decreasing** exponential curve.

Example 3

Movie tickets now average $9.75 a ticket, but are increasing 15% per year. How much will they cost 5 years from now?

The equation to use is: $y = ab^x$. The initial value $a = 9.75$. The multiplier b is always found by adding the percent increase (as a decimal) to the number 1 (100%), so $b = 1 + 0.15 = 1.15$. The time is $x = 5$. Substituting into the equation and using a calculator for the calculations: $y = ab^x = 9.75(1.15)^5 \approx 19.61$. In five years movie tickets will average about $19.61.

Example 4

A powerful computer is $2000, but on the average loses 20% of its value each year. How much will it be worth 4 years from now?

The equation to use is: $y = ab^x$. The initial value $a = 2000$. In this case the value is decreasing so multiplier b is always found by subtracting the percent decrease from the number 1 (100%), so $b = 1 - 0.2 = 0.8$. The time is $x = 4$. Substituting into the equation and using a calculator for the calculations: $y = ab^x = 2000(0.8)^4 = 819.2$. In four years the computer will only be worth $819.20.

Example 5

Dinner at your grandfather's favorite restaurant now costs $25.25 and has been increasing steadily at 4% per year. How much did it cost 35 *years ago* when he was courting your grandmother?

The equation is the same as above and $a = 25.25$, $b = 1.04$, but since we want to go back in time, $x = -35$. A common mistake is to think that $b = 0.96$. The equation is $y = ab^x = 25.25(1.04)^{-35} \approx 6.40$.

Example 6

If a gallon of milk costs $3 now and the price is increasing 10% per year, how long before milk costs $10 a gallon?

In this case we know the starting value $a = 3$, the multiplier $b = 1.1$, the final value $y = 10$, but not the time x. Substituting into the equation we get $3(1.1)^x = 10$. To solve this, you will probably need to guess and check with your calculator. Doing so yields $x \approx 12.6$ years. In Algebra 2 you will learn to solve these equations without guess and check.

Problems

Make a table of values and draw a graph of each exponential function.

1. $y = 4(0.5)^x$
2. $y = 2(3)^x$
3. $y = 5(1.2)^x$
4. $y = 10\left(\frac{2}{3}\right)^x$

5. The number of bacteria present in a colony at 12 noon is 180 and the bacteria grows at a rate of 22% per hour. How many will be present at 8 p.m.?

6. A house purchased for $226,000 has lost 4% of its value each year for the past five years. What is it worth now?

7. A 1970 comic book has appreciated 10% per year and originally sold for $0.35. What will it be worth in 2010?

8. A certain car depreciates at 15% per year. Six years ago it was purchased for $21,000. What is it worth now?

9. Inflation is at a rate of 7% per year. Today Janelle's favorite bread costs $3.79. What would it have cost ten years ago?

10. Ryan's motorcycle is now worth $2500. It has decreased in value 12% each year since it was purchased. If he bought it four years ago, what did it cost new?

11. The cost of a high definition television now averages $1200, but the cost is decreasing about 15% per year. In how many years will the cost be under $500?

12. A two-bedroom house in Nashville is worth $110,000. If it appreciates at 2.5% per year, when will it be worth $200,000?

13. Last year the principal's car was worth $28,000. Next year it will be worth $25,270. What is the annual rate of depreciation? What is the car worth now?

14. A concert has been sold out for weeks, and as the date of the concert draws closer, the price of the ticket increases. The cost of a pair of tickets was $150 yesterday and is $162 today. Assuming that the cost continues to increase at this rate:

    a.   What is the daily rate of increase? What is the multiplier?

    b.   What will be the cost one week from now, the day before the concert?

    c.   What was the cost two weeks ago?

Answers

1. $y = 4\left(\frac{1}{2}\right)^x$

2. $y = 2 \cdot 3^x$

3. $y = 5(1.2)^x$

4. $y = 10\left(\frac{2}{3}\right)^x$

5. ≈ 883 6. $184,274   7. $15.84   8. $7,920

9. $1.92   10. $4,169   11. ≈ 5 years   12. ≈ 24 years

13.   5%, $26,600   14.   a. 8%, 1.08   b. $277.64   c. $55.15

Problems

Solve these various types of equations.

1. $2(x-3)+2=-4$

2. $6-12x=108$

3. $3x-11=0$

4. $0=2x-5$

5. $y=2x-3$
   $x+y=15$

6. $ax-b=0$
   (solve for x)

7. $0=(2x-5)(x+3)$

8. $2(2x-1)=-x+5$

9. $x^2+5^2=13^2$

10. $2x+1=7x-15$

11. $\frac{5-2x}{3}=\frac{x}{5}$

12. $2x-3y+9=0$
    (solve for y)

13. $x^2+5x+6=0$

14. $x^2=y$
    $100=y$

15. $x-y=7$
    $y=2x-1$

16. $x^2-4x=0$

17. $x^2-6=-2$

18. $\frac{x}{2}+\frac{x}{3}=2$

19. $x^2+7x+9=3$

20. $y=x+3$
    $x+2y=3$

21. $3x^2+7x+2=0$

22. $\frac{x}{x+1}=\frac{5}{7}$

23. $x^2+2x-4=0$

24. $\frac{1}{x}+\frac{1}{3x}=2$

25. $3x+y=5$
    $x-y=11$

26. $y=-\frac{3}{4}x+4$
    $\frac{1}{4}x-y=8$

27. $3x^2=8x$

28. $|x|=4$

29. $\frac{2}{3}x+1=\frac{1}{2}x-3$

30. $x^2-4x=5$

31. $3x+5y=15$
    (solve for y)

32. $(3x)^2+x^2=15^2$

33. $y=11$
    $y=2x^2+3x-9$

34. $(x+2)(x+3)(x-4)=0$

35. $|x+6|=8$

36. $2(x+3)=y+2$
    $y+2=8x$

37. $2x+3y=13$
    $x-2y=-11$

38. $2x^2=-x+7$

39. $1-\frac{5}{6x}=\frac{x}{6}$

40. $\frac{x-1}{5}=\frac{3}{x+1}$

41. $\sqrt{2x+1}=5$

42. $2|2x-1|+3=7$

43. $\sqrt{3x-1}+1=7$

44. $(x+3)^2=49$

45. $\frac{4x-1}{x-1}=x+1$

Solve these various types of inequalities.

46. $4x - 2 \leq 6$

47. $4 - 3(x + 2) \geq 19$

48. $\frac{x}{2} > \frac{3}{7}$

49. $3(x + 2) \geq -9$

50. $-\frac{2}{3}x < 6$

51. $y < 2x - 3$

52. $|x| > 4$

53. $x^2 - 6x + 8 \leq 0$

54. $|x + 3| > 5$

55. $2x^2 - 4x \geq 0$

56. $y \leq -\frac{2}{3}x + 2$

57. $y < -x + 2$
    $y \leq 3x - 6$

58. $|2x - 1| \leq 9$

59. $5 - 3(x - 1) \geq -x + 2$

60. $y \leq 4x + 16$
    $y > -\frac{4}{3}x - 4$

Answers

1. $x = 0$

2. $x = -8.5$

3. $x = \frac{11}{3}$

4. $x = \frac{5}{2}$

5. $(6, 9)$

6. $x = \frac{b}{a}$

7. $x = \frac{5}{2}, -3$

8. $x = \frac{7}{5}$

9. $x = \pm 12$

10. $x = \frac{16}{5}$

11. $x = \frac{25}{13}$

12. $y = \frac{2}{3}x + 3$

13. $x = -2, -3$

14. $(\pm 10, 100)$

15. $(-6, -13)$

16. $x = 0, 4$

17. $x = \pm 2$

18. $x = \frac{12}{5}$

19. $x = -1, -6$

20. $(-1, 2)$

21. $x = -\frac{1}{3}, -2$

22. $x = \frac{5}{2}$

23. $x = \frac{-2 \pm \sqrt{20}}{2}$

24. $x = \frac{2}{3}$

25. $(4, -7)$

26. $(12, -5)$

27. $x = 0, \frac{8}{3}$

28. $x = \pm 4$

29. $x = -24$

30. $x = 5, -1$

31. $y = -\frac{3}{5}x + 3$

32. $x \approx \pm 4.74$

33. $(-4, 11)$ and $(\frac{5}{2}, 11)$

34. $x = -2, -3, 4$

35. $x = 2, -14$

36. $(1, 6)$

37. $(-1, 5)$

38. $x = \frac{1 \pm \sqrt{57}}{4}$

39. $x = 1, 5$

40. $x = \pm 4$

41. $x = 12$

42. $x = \frac{3}{2}, -\frac{1}{2}$

43. $x = \frac{37}{3}$

44. $x = 4, -10$

45. $x = 0, 4$

46. $x \leq 2$

47. $x \leq -7$

48. $x > \frac{6}{7}$

49. $x \geq -5$

50. $x > -9$

51. See next page.

52. $x > 4, x < -4$

53. $2 \leq x \leq 4$

54. $x > 2$ or $x < -8$

55. $x \leq 0$ or $x \geq 2$

56. See next page.

57. See next page.

58. $-4 \leq x \leq 5$

59. $x \leq 3$

60. See next page.

51.

56.

57.

60.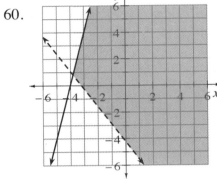